SCIENTIFIC MANPOWER

SCIENTIFIC MANPOWER

by

JOYCE ALEXANDER

HILGER & WATTS LTD
LONDON

PRINTED IN GREAT BRITAIN BY ROBERT MACLEHOSE AND CO. LTD
THE UNIVERSITY PRESS, GLASGOW

PREFACE

A Committee known as the Science and Industry Committee was set up in 1952 by the British Association for the Advancement of Science (later joined by the Royal Society of Arts and the Nuffield Foundation as co-sponsors), for the purpose of examining what factors impeded or were important in the rate at which scientific discoveries were adopted by industry. A research staff was recruited, of which I was a member. As I had worked in industry in a technical capacity, and had also some experience of training for industry by virtue of evening lecturing, I tended to concentrate on the shortage of scientists and engineers. This book is based on material gathered while in the Committee's employ, and I would like to acknowledge its permission to use this data.

On attempting a serious study of the shortage of scientists and technologists, one is confronted by a mass of material, much of solid value but much more mere subjective speculation. In an attempt to assemble facts I visited Universities and Technical Colleges in all parts of the country, and talked to many leading professional and educational people. I also investigated the position in other countries, visiting representative institutions in France, Italy, Germany and Switzerland.

This book is naturally concerned primarily with the special problems of the United Kingdom. Among these I have perhaps dwelt overmuch on the position of my sex. If so I would beg the reader's indulgence.

I should like to thank the many people who have helped me, both in discussion and in answering what must have seemed tedious questionnaires, the Nuffield Foundation which made a special grant and enabled me to investigate conditions on the Continent at first hand, and Professor C. F. Carter, Director of Research of the Science and Industry Committee, whose suggestions and penetrating criticisms were of inestimable value.

BELFAST
AUGUST, 1959

JOYCE ALEXANDER

ACKNOWLEDGEMENTS

For permission to quote copyright extracts and statistics, and to use their research material, I wish to thank the following:

Mrs Margot Jefferys, the Editors of the *British Journal of Sociology*, and Messrs Routledge and Kegan Paul, Ltd (*Married Women in the Higher Grades of the Civil Service*).

Mrs Constance Arreger and the Editors of *The New Scientist* ('*Why so few women scientists and technologists?*').

Mrs Judith Hubback and Messrs William Heinemann, Ltd (*Wives who went to College*).

Miss E. M. Harris and the Institute of Personnel Management (*Married Women in Industry*).

Miss Viola Klein, Mme Alva Myrdal, and Messrs Routledge and Kegan Paul, Ltd (*Women's Two Roles*).

Dr Margaret Mead and Messrs Victor Gollanz, Ltd (*Male and Female*).

Miss Verena Holmes and the Women's Engineering Society (*Engineering Training for Women*).

W. E. Egner, D. Young, Esq., and the Liverpool University Press (*The Staffing of Grammar Schools*).

The Federation of British Industries (*Industry and the Technical Colleges*).

Political and Economic Planning (*Salaries of Graduates in Industry*).

R. P. Linstead, Esq., C.B.E., F.R.S. (*The Future of the Imperial College*).

Penguin Books Ltd (*Child Care and the Growth of Love*).

T. J. Drakeley, Esq., C.B.E., D.Sc., Ph.D., F.R.I.C., F.I.R.I. (*Technical Education and Our Future*).

Nicholas De Witt, Esq. (*Soviet Professional Manpower*).

CONTENTS

CHAPTER I

THE SHORTAGE OF TECHNICALLY TRAINED MANPOWER

The problem

The shortage of scientists, engineers, and technologists, has become one of the most widely discussed topics of the day, for articles pin-pointing certain aspects of the problem appear in learned journals and in the Press. Much of the writing is of a speculative nature, but of one thing everyone is sure, more scientifically trained people are needed than are being produced at the moment. Many complete or partial remedies have been suggested, some practical, some not.

Recently more and more statistics have been quoted on technologists and technologists-in-training in other countries. While these figures do show that the United Kingdom is lagging far behind in this respect, too much significance must not be given to them. Britain is a small country whose economy is very different from that of the United States or Russia. There is no correct number of scientists per thousand of the population; each country must achieve its own balance. However, when the disparity is great, as is apparent in some fields, a certain amount of thought and attention is clearly necessary.

It is well known that industry feels itself starved of trained people in many fields. A greater shortage is to be found in the teaching profession, and it is obvious that this must affect the future supply of scientists and engineers to industry.

Discoveries in the laboratory (which are very frequent these days) need many people. There have to be, in addition to the research staff from whom the idea emanated in the first place, administrators capable of appreciating the discovery and assessing its value, development and production engineers to carry the scheme through to the final stages.

Some firms are trying to recruit engineers from other

A   A.S.M.

countries to make up staff deficiencies, but most countries now are themselves experiencing the same shortages. A recent report,[1] issued jointly by the Ministry of Labour and National Service, and the Advisory Council on Scientific Policy, estimated both the short-term and the long-term demands for scientific manpower. Often these estimates are little more than inspired guesses, but they are the best available.

Included in the report was the following table showing the present distribution of scientists and engineers:

	Qualified scientists	Qualified engineers	Total qualified scientists and engineers	Total no. of engineers with H.N.C., H.N.D., or equivalent only
Manufacturing Industry[2]	17,050	37,000	54,050	22,790
Nationalized Industries[3]	2,420	14,660	17,080	5,330
Central Government	5,800	8,050	13,850	1,710
Local Authorities	350	6,330	6,680	320
Education	25,610	2,430	28,040	—
TOTAL	51,230	68,470	119,700	30,150

These figures do not include people employed in agriculture, the non-nationalized part of the mining and transport industries, shipping, the distributive trades, and miscellaneous service industries. Self-employed persons and persons employed by firms of consultants were also excluded, as were those in manufacturing and contracting establishments with fewer than one hundred workers.[4] Rough estimates of those in these groups and in the Armed Forces gave the following figures:

	Qualified scientists	Qualified engineers	Total
(a) In employment covered by the enquiry	51,230	68,470	119,700
(b) In other employment	5,000	10,000	15,000
GRAND TOTAL	56,230	78,470	134,700

[1] *Scientific and Engineering Manpower in Great Britain: A report on the number and distribution of scientists and engineers now employed in Great Britain, and a study of the likely trend in the future demand for scientific and engineering manpower*, H.M.S.O., London, 1956.
[2] Including the building and contracting industry, and industrial research associations.
[3] Including Atomic Energy Authority.
[4] It was also noted that certain types of technologist (e.g. textile technologist) had been omitted.

It was found that of the qualified scientists and engineers, 12,000 were employed in the electrical engineering industry, 8,300 in the chemical industry, 4,300 in aircraft manufacture, and 6,700 in the manufacture of machinery.

The report also noted:

Of the 13,850 scientists and engineers in Government employment, just over one half are in the defence departments (including the Ministry of Supply), just over a quarter in the civil departments and one sixth in the research departments.

Estimates of shortage: short-term demand

Employers in a sample group were asked for their requirements three years from the time of the survey; from this the following tables were obtained:

	Number employed 1956	1959 requirements stated by employers	
		Number	Percentage increase over 1956
Manufacturing Industry	48,800	67,000	37
Building and Contracting	3,800	5,000	32
Research Associations	1,400	1,740	24
Nationalized Industries and Atomic Energy Authority	17,100	20,900	22
TOTAL INDUSTRY	71,100	94,640	33

	Estimate of 1959 requirements	Present numbers	Percentage increase over 1956
1. Central Government	8,500	7,600	12
(a) Defence Departments	4,450	3,900	14
(b) Civil Departments	2,900	2,350	23
TOTAL	15,850	13,850	14·5
2. Local Authorities	6,700	8,500	27
3. Teaching			
(a) Universities	4,350	3,250	34
(b) Schools, etc.	26,700	24,800	8
TOTAL	31,050	28,050	11
GRAND TOTAL	48,600	50,400	14

The future requirements of the different types of scientists and engineers, as shown by this survey, were:

	Number employed in 1956	Estimated demand in 1959	Increase over 1956	Percentage increase over 1956
Scientists				
Biologists	4,800	5,400	600	12·5
Chemists	20,700	25,200	4,500	22
Geologists	900	1,100	200	22
Mathematicians	11,500	13,000	1,500	13
Physicists	10,500	12,900	2,400	23
Other Scientists	2,800	3,100	300	11
TOTAL SCIENTISTS	51,200	60,700	9,500	18·5
Engineers				
Chemical	1,500	2,200	700	47
Civil	12,800	16,200	3,400	27
Electrical	17,800	22,900	5,100	29
Mining	3,800	4,800	1,000	26
Mechanical and others	27,000	35,800	8,800	33
Metallurgists	3,200	4,400	1,200	38
Engineers in teaching	2,400	3,000	600	25
TOTAL ENGINEERS	68,500	89,300	20,800	30
TOTAL SCIENTISTS AND ENGINEERS	119,700	150,000	30,300	26

Estimates of shortage: long term demand

In the same report there was an estimate of the long-term demand for scientists and engineers. To maintain an annual rate of growth of 4 per cent in industrial output it would be necessary to increase the number of qualified scientists and engineers 'from the present level of about 135,000 to somewhere in the region of 220,000 in 1966—an increase of over 60 per cent'. It was found that an increase of about 70 per cent in the number of engineers and 50 per cent in the number of scientists would be needed, and that to produce the required increase the annual output of trained scientists and engineers would have to double by 1970.

Object of survey

This present survey is concerned largely with the means of training these new scientists and engineers. Does the training achieve its purpose? What changes have been made recently, and what difficulties have been encountered? What difficulties may be expected in the future? There are many comparisons with the way in which people are trained in other countries, not with an attitude that Britain is always wrong, but to see what can be learnt from the examples and mistakes of others.

CHAPTER II

PATHS TO SCIENTIFIC AND TECHNOLOGICAL CAREERS

Definition of terms

One of the difficulties experienced in any discussion about scientists, technologists, engineers, and technicians, is the satisfactory definition of the terms. This arises from the widely differing methods of training which are possible for these occupations. In general, the professional engineer is regarded as being of graduate level, although he may not have received his training at a university.

The established professional institutions have acquired reputations which usually make membership of the relevant body a prerequisite for employment at a professional level. The Institutions of Mechanical Engineers, Electrical Engineers and Civil Engineers, use this definition :

A professional engineer is competent by virtue of his fundamental education and training to apply the scientific method and outlook to the analysis and solution of engineering problems. He is able to assume personal responsibility for the development and application of engineering science, notably in research, designing, construction, manufacturing, superintending, managing, and in the education of the engineer. His work is predominantly intellectual and varied, and not of a routine mental or physical character. It requires the exercise of original thought and judgement and the ability to supervise the technical and administrative work of others.

His education will have been such as to make him capable of closely and continuously following progess in his branch of engineering science by consulting newly published work on a world-wide basis, assimilating such information and applying it independently. He is thus placed in a position to make contributions to the development of engineering science and its applications.

His education and training will have been such that he will have acquired a broad and general appreciation of the engineering sciences as well as thorough insight into the special features of his own branch. In due time he will be able to give authoritative technical advice, and to assume responsibility for the direction of important tasks in his own branch.

The emphasis is essentially on the results of education, since the aim is to leave the way open to qualification regardless of age and schooling.

A further classification is that of 'engineering technician' which is defined in the following way by the above-mentioned professional institutions :[1]

An engineering technician is one who can apply in a responsible manner proven techniques which are commonly understood by those who are expert in a branch of engineering, or those techniques specially prescribed by professional engineers.

Under general professional engineering direction, or following established engineering techniques, he is capable of carrying out duties which may be found among the list of examples set out below.

In carrying out many of these duties, competent supervision of the work of skilled craftsmen will be necessary. The techniques employed demand acquired experience and knowledge of a particular branch of engineering, combined with the ability to work out the details of a task in the light of well-established practice.

An engineering technician requires an education and training sufficient to enable him to understand the reasons for and the purposes of the operation for which he is responsible.

The following duties are typical of those carried out by engineering technicians :

Working on design and development of engineering plant and structures ; erecting and commissioning of engineering equipment and structures ; engineering drawing ; estimating, testing and inspecting engineering construction and equipment ; use of surveying instruments ; operating, maintaining and repairing engineering machinery, plant and engineering services and locating defects therein ; activities connected with research and development, testing of materials and components and sales engineering, servicing equipment, and advising consumers.

The term 'scientist' is rarely used other than to describe someone who has received a university training in one of the branches of science.

Educational background of scientists and engineers

There are many ways to a scientific or engineering career. In this country the majority of children sit at eleven-plus a qualifying examination, which is supposed to select the most appropriate education for each child. The choice is between secondary grammar, offering what is called an 'academic' education ; secondary technical, for those whose abilities are more practical ; and secondary modern, where a general

[1] It has been suggested that this definition of technician represents what is desirable rather than actual fact, and so a further definition of a somewhat lower grade is necessary.

education is available terminating at fifteen for most pupils. Our system is so flexible that it is possible to reach either professional engineering or engineering technician status by attending any one of these three types of school. Graduate scientist status is usually reached by the straight path through grammar school and university.

The most direct path to professional engineering or technological status is by means of either a public or a grammar school and then a university. Within this framework there are many possible variations; an undergraduate may read for a degree in any of a wide range of scientific and technological subjects. The role of the schools is discussed in Chapter III; that of the universities in Chapter IV.

Academic education alone does not make an engineer; practical training is also necessary. This may be left either to the post-graduate stage, or may be introduced between school and university, or may take place during university vacations.

It is possible for the public- or grammar-school boy to receive his professional training in the technical college. This is now encouraged by State awards but it is not yet widespread since some schoolboys have a natural desire for a university career, and are encouraged in this by many local authorities who provide generous scholarships. Technical colleges cannot hope to match the prestige of the universities; they cannot compete successfully for lecturers in subjects common to both; and often they cannot provide the same amenities as the university. It is hoped that the establishment of the Colleges of Advanced Technology (see Chapter IV) will help to remedy these difficulties.

As these new colleges will carry out no work below university level, they will require an adequate standard of preliminary education. This, it is hoped, will attract more boys from the public and grammar schools. For many boys, however, the technical college offers the only possible form of further education. This may be because matriculation requirements have not been met, because of financial difficulties (although sometimes university education is cheaper and more accessible than that of the technical college), or because of a desire to study part time only. Part-time study may take place by means of evening classes, day-release from employment, or sandwich courses. The latter consist of periods of full-time academic training, interspersed with periods of full-time practical training, each phase lasting several months. They may be either works-based or college-based. In the former the students are engaged on leaving school by a particular firm which arranges with a nearby technical college for their theoretical training. Some firms pay a definite salary throughout both the works and college periods, and also cover all expenses; others pay a salary during the works period only, and make some form of allowance for the college period. College-based courses are run solely by the college, who make arrangements with firms for appropriate employment for their students. They generally go to a different firm each time. These students usually receive a salary during their employment periods, and probably a scholarship during the remainder of the time.

At present the grammar-school boy who goes to a technical college will rarely have proceeded beyond the Ordinary Level of the General Certificate of Education (G.C.E. 'O' level). Those who have taken Advanced Level ('A' level) subjects will tend to go to a university. Now, however, it is hoped that an increasing proportion of 'A' level pupils will enter the new Colleges of Advanced Technology.

It is possible for technical-school pupils to achieve graduate status by attending either a university or a technical college, the latter being more common. Here questions of ability arise. In theory boys who attend a technical school are not necessarily of lower intelligence than those at a grammar school, since the eleven-plus examination is supposed to select the most appropriate education for each child. In practice, however, the most able children are generally selected at eleven, and a second layer of ability is then chosen from the remainder approximately two years later.

Most technical-school boys enter industry around the age of sixteen; they may enter either a works or a more general ap-

prenticeship, and continue to study by means of day-release
from employment and through evening classes. Such classes
lead normally to the Ordinary National Certificate, and after
further study to the Higher National Certificate, which is
approximately of University Intermediate standard. It is then
possible to work for an external degree, or for the new qualification, a Diploma in Technology.

At a lower level, the technical-school boy may sit the examinations of the City and Guilds of London Institute, which are
more of a craft nature than the National Certificate examinations.

The boy who leaves a modern school at fifteen or later may
also continue his education at a technical college, and in theory
it is possible for him to reach graduate status too. He will, however, probably attend craft classes.

There is still a great deal of wastage in part-time courses for
technicians and craftsmen. The reasons may be ill-health,
travelling difficulties, lack of encouragement from the employer,
change of job, shift work, working away from home, the need
to work overtime, difficult home conditions, or a combination
of two or more of these. Well-organised day-release classes can
do much to eliminate these difficulties.

A number of technical colleges have been preparing students
for the Ordinary and Higher National Diplomas. These are
awarded after full-time study, and are the equivalents of the
National Certificates, which are for part-time work only. The
numbers taking such courses have always been limited since
most people who wished to continue full-time education stayed
on at school and then went to a university. In addition these
qualifications were not regarded as being sufficiently different
from the National Certificates to justify full-time study.

In general, a degree plus the appropriate practical experience
will lead to professional status; the National Certificates to
technician status; and lower examinations to craft or sub-
technician status. However, it is possible to move up from one
grade to the next.

There is still considerable doubt about the efficiency of the
eleven-plus examination; this arises largely from the belief that

the secondary modern school is for those children who are un-suited to an academic education, and so academic talent is either neglected or not expected. In fact, in some modern schools, boys and girls are beginning to take subjects at G.C.E. 'O' level; some transfer to a grammar school and end up in a university. In addition, many of them are able to gain the Higher National Certificate by part-time study after leaving school.

Thus by keeping the way open to all we are preventing wast-age due to an over-rigid system.

Educational background of scientists and engineers in other countries; comparison with the United Kingdom

In most European countries, the formal education which a child receives determines both his future career and social status; there is rarely much opportunity for moving from one stratum to the next. This may be well illustrated by the title 'engineer', which is usually a protected one, and is reserved for appropriately-trained university graduates. There is little part-time study at a high level, and attendance at a school similar to our grammar school and then at a university is usually essential for a professional career. Technicians are specially trained too, and are rarely able to attain professional status.

In this country the essence of education for industry is flexibility; a boy may attend appropriate classes at a technical college whatever his previous education may have been, and no limits are set to the heights which he may reach. This is at once one of the main strengths and main weaknesses of our engin-eering education. In countries where the term 'engineer' is pro-tected and guarded jealously, the engineer occupies an honoured place in the community. In Britain the title is not only open to all, but is badly misused. 'Engineers strike for more pay' is a typical caption to be found in the daily Press; those referred to are usually skilled, semi-skilled and unskilled workers. This is not conducive to increasing the prestige of engineers; contrast it with our respect for doctors and lawyers, where we know that precise standards are applied.

What is probably needed is a compromise; leave the way open, but protect the title 'engineer', and confine it to those who have reached appropriate standards. This should help to remedy the shortages.

CHAPTER III

THE PUBLIC AND GRAMMAR SCHOOLS

Scientific careers and the public and grammar schools

A high proportion of our most able children go to the grammar schools. From these schools do the scientific and technological professions receive their fair share of the talent available?

Allegations are made from all sides that some headmasters (and headmistresses) attempt to direct their brighter pupils to the study of the arts in their final years at school, because of the prestige which is supposed to be attached to such subjects. It is also suggested that specialization (i.e. the dropping of some subjects in order to concentrate on others) now takes place at a junior level in the school, so that the pupils concerned drop subjects, particularly mathematics and the sciences, which they may require at a later stage. The shortage of science teachers or of laboratories and equipment has caused a great number of schools to cut down their science classes, and even to stop teaching science altogether.

Attitudes to science teaching in schools

Scientists have had to fight hard for the recognition of their subjects as suitable ones for teaching in school. At the Commission on Public Schools, which was appointed in 1862, Michael Faraday was asked the following question:

Have you ever had occasion to enquire or have you formed to yourself any opinion as to why these studies should have been so neglected at our schools?

He replied,

. . . As far as I can see it is only a matter of habit and prejudice, derived, and which must be derived as things progress, from pre-existing conditions. The present mode of instruction in literature has been established for ages; and the other knowledge, which is not altogether new knowledge, but of which the immense body is new, and most of the applications of which are new, has not yet had time to make itself familiar and become appreciated. . . .

Sir Charles Lyell, the geologist, said in his reply to this question,

> ... I think that the schools being preparatory, in a great measure, to the universities, they frame their system in regard to those subjects which are to obtain the chief rewards, prizes and honours at the university. Although a large proportion of the boys at our larger schools do not go to the universities (I do not know what proportion, but I know that it is very large) nevertheless the system is planned as if all were going there, and whatever the plan adopted at the universities, and particularly whatever may be the matriculation or entrance examination to the university, that will in no small degree govern what is taught in public schools, if any branch of knowledge is omitted. . . .

Scientific subjects were grudgingly included in the curriculum but were not encouraged for many years. The grammar schools followed suit, and only in recent years has science become respectable.

The remarkable amount of publicity given to science in the last few years has had a definite effect on the schools, and the old 'snob' ideas about science seem to have broken down. The criterion now is the ability to study a science subject.

Enquiry on specialization, science teaching and career decisions

There have been many complaints about over-specialization in schools; critics say that vital choices of subject and of career are made at too early a stage; headmasters and headmistresses say that some specialization is essential for the selection of subjects for the 'O' level examinations of the G.C.E., and that extreme specialization is then necessary for the 'A' level. The Science and Industry Committee decided to institute a special enquiry into this subject to find out what was happening in the schools. In June 1956 a questionnaire (see Appendix I) on certain aspects of specialization, on science teaching, and on career decisions, was sent to 332 independent, direct grant, and maintained schools in Great Britain. Satisfactory replies were received from 198 schools.

The following table shows the ages at which specialization is necessary at schools in the given sample:

Age at which specialization takes place	Proportion of all schools	Proportion of boys' schools	Proportion of girls' schools	Proportion of co-educational schools
13+	9·6%	14·1%	3·4%	17·1%
14+	40·7%	17·2%	53·9%	51·2%
15+	21·7%	26·6%	20·2%	19·5%
16+ (after 'O' Level)	19·4%	35·9%	12·4%	9·8%
Schools in which effectively no science is offered	5·1%	1·6%	9·0%	2·4%
New schools, or insufficient information	3·5%	4·7%	1·1%	0%

Notes
1. The percentages have been taken to one decimal place; in consequence the figures in the columns do not all add to give 100 per cent.
2. The 'effectively no science offered' designation means either:
  (*a*) that General Science, Biology and Physics-with-Chemistry are the only subjects offered at 'O' level.
  or (*b*) that Physics and Chemistry are not started until after 'O' level has been attained in other subjects; therefore many pupils will leave school without any acquaintance with science.

It may be seen from the table that in just over half of the schools pupils must make their selection at thirteen-plus or fourteen-plus; this takes place mainly in the girls' and co-educational schools, while the situation is not quite so serious in boys' schools. It may also be noticed that 9 per cent of the girls' schools do not offer an effective chance of a scientific education.

The selection of subjects, as we have seen, is usually made one or two years before G.C.E. 'O' level which is taken at about sixteen. In some schools this means a choice between literary and scientific subjects; in others a basic group covering both sides is carried to 'O' level. At one school all boys offer English, History, French, Latin, Mathematics, Physics, Chemistry and either Greek or German at 'O' level; at other schools (mostly independent ones) three or four 'O' level subjects (English, Mathematics, French, Latin, etc.,) are taken at fourteen or fifteen, and then a selected group is taken to 'O' or 'A' level.

The other ways in which the necessary choices are made show considerable variation. In some schools definite alternatives are given, such as Latin or Physics, Domestic Science or Biology, etc. The dropping of Latin for a science subject can be dangerous, for it has often to be taken up again after 'O' level as it is needed to gain entrance to a university. In other schools a completely free choice of subjects is offered, and the timetable is then drawn up to fit these choices.

Most educational bodies recommend that pupils should offer their best subjects at 'A' level only, and this does happen in a few schools. In general, however, parents and the pupils themselves like to base their decisions about extreme specialization on 'O' level results; there is also the feeling that, either for academic or financial reasons, 'A' level may never be achieved, and that in consequence 'O' level should be taken first.

The amount of science taught in schools varies greatly. In most boys' and co-educational schools, Physics and Chemistry are offered as separate subjects at 'O' level, while in many girls' schools, Physics-with-Chemistry is offered by the so-called 'scientists'; in many other schools the only scientific subjects taught are General Science I and II, which offer very little foundation for a scientific career.

Headmistresses of girls' schools have many problems. Science mistresses are in very short supply, and it is often necessary to reduce drastically the number taking science. Scientific equipment is poor, and so it is difficult to organise practical classes properly. All this leads to a very small Science Sixth, and in consequence there arises a vicious circle; it does not appear economic to have many science specialists on the staff, even if they are obtainable, and adequate advanced training is rarely available.

Scientific syllabuses for the General Certificate of Education

A study of the syllabus for the 'A' level scientific subjects in G.C.E. shows that definite mathematical and scientific ability is needed, and this is reasonable as the examination is designed for university candidates. The 'O' level General Science papers and the Physics-with-Chemistry paper involve only elementary concepts and should be well within the capabilities of even the most unscientific pupils; similarly Mathematics and Chemistry should not present much difficulty; on the other hand, 'O' level Physics and Applied Mathematics do demand the ability to think in abstract terms, and are in consequence probably beyond many people.

Specialization and university entrance requirements

Schoolteachers are aware of the dangers of over-specialization, but they claim that it is necessary to meet university requirements. One headmistress, who had completed my questionnaire, told me that her girls take a very wide range of subjects at 'O' level, which she thinks is ideal for those who will then leave, but this does tend to jeopardize the brilliant girl's chance of a place in a university.

More and more people are becoming conscious that there may be too much specialization in schools; that we insist on early specialization and then complain about illiterate under-graduates. Many educationists are beginning to demand a more general education in the schools, leaving the specialization to the university. It is pointed out that this is particularly neces-sary now that many grammar-school pupils come from homes in which any deficiencies in general education cannot be remedied. It is also suggested that the good all-rounder might be more likely to study science if it did not involve giving up at fourteen a subject such as history.

At present the schools tend to cater mainly for the uni-versity candidate. In the upper forms university and faculty entrance requirements are all-important. It is worth asking if there is sufficient provision in Sixth Forms for those who are not university candidates, but who have no wish to cease their general education at sixteen. A general Sixth-Form course would be beneficial to them and could also benefit university entrants if qualifications for entrance were relaxed.

It does seem that vital choices are being made too young, and it is difficult to assess just what loss to scientific occupations this represents, but it must mean that many pupils do not do enough science to excite their interest. The longer the choice between Science and Arts can be deferred, the greater the chance that people will make choices in line with their true abilities.

Loss to scientific occupations due to premature leaving from grammar schools

There is not only the question of what is being taught at 'O' and 'A' levels; we must also consider those children who embark on a grammar-school career but never reach this level. The Report of the Central Advisory Council for Education[1] shows that out of twenty-seven thousand pupils who were considered suitable for advanced courses in English grammar schools, ten thousand did not remain at school long enough to take such courses; of these ten thousand, over five thousand could have followed advanced courses in mathematics and science.

There are a number of reasons for premature leaving from schools, and a number of possible causes are analysed in the Early Leaving Report. One of the main findings of their enquiry was that this problem was intimately linked with social position, and that the child whose parents had not been educated beyond the primary stage was likely to leave school earlier than one with a professional background. It was pointed out that in many cases the decision to leave was made by the child who was given a free choice by the parents, but the report went on to add that '. . . in this context neutrality on the part of the parents is likely to tell in favour of leaving, since ephemeral irritations and ambitions may well be uppermost in an adolescent mind. It should be the function of the parents to look further ahead.'

It is not always the home environment which influences the length of school life; relatives, family friends, and neighbours, have a marked effect and may directly or indirectly influence parents in this respect.

It is not of course always because of parental indifference that children leave school too soon; for many, financial reasons are all-important. The Early Leaving Report has advised that generous maintenance allowances on a need basis should be paid to those pupils who remain at school beyond the age of

[1] *Early Leaving.* A Report of the Central Advisory Council for Education. H.M.S.O., London, 1954.

sixteen. The present allowances do not qualify for the adjective 'generous'.

There is a great deal of variation in the provision of grammar-school places; in some areas the proportion may be as low as 9 per cent, in others as high as 44 per cent. It does not seem reasonable to assume that the number of children capable of benefiting from a grammar-school education varies as much as this, and hence it is probable that many children who would be suited to a grammar school are denied the opportunity to attend one.

Shortages of laboratory accommodation and of scientific apparatus in schools

A large number of the schools in our sample were experiencing a shortage of laboratory accommodation and of scientific apparatus, and in many cases this imposed a limit on the number of children who could attend science classes. The problem is particularly acute in the independent and direct grant schools which do not receive public money for capital works.

Industry was perturbed by this state of affairs, and so, in 1946, a number of large firms combined to set up the Industrial Fund for the Advancement of Scientific Education in Schools. From this fund grants were to be made to independent and direct grant schools for the provision of new buildings and laboratory equipment, and the conversion and modernization of existing buildings.

Within eighteen months the Fund's Committee completed its work, and had guaranteed to 328 boys' and girls' schools capital grants totalling £3,159,669.

Shortage of science teachers

Replies to the questionnaire showed that in many places it was difficult to obtain science teachers. This problem is discussed fully in Chapter VIII, and it is only necessary to say here that an insufficient number of children receive inspired teaching from first-rate science teachers, and that this must affect their decision whether or not to continue studying science.

Choice of career, and vocational guidance

The Education Act has meant that many children are educated to a standard beyond that reached by their parents; in particular a number of grammar-school pupils are the first generation in their family to receive any education beyond the primary stage.

This raises special difficulties about the choice of career, for there are some parents who will not have sufficient knowledge of the qualifications needed and the rewards to be gained in many of the professional careers. For these children vocational guidance is particularly important. To find out about this a questionnaire (Appendix 2) was sent to sixty County Youth Employment Offices, and from them forty-nine replies were received (an 82 per cent response).

From the replies it was apparent that in more than half of those grammar schools which used the Youth Employment Service, advice on careers was not given until the year in which the G.C.E. 'O' level examinations were taken. Half of the Youth Employment Offices thought that parents had a great deal of influence on their children's choice of career; a rather smaller number agreed that the choice was related to parental occupation. The majority of them had come across very few instances of children who had made a wrong choice of subject, and said that the most common mistake of schoolchildren was the dropping of mathematics.

However, the Youth Employment Service does seem to be designed mainly for the secondary modern schools, whereas the grammar-school pupil often needs as much guidance.

There is a particular risk that parents who work at a skilled or unskilled level in industry will be suspicious of industrial careers at the professional level; they will be anxious for their children to enter the professions which to them have a particularly high prestige since definite educational standards are required. The opportunities which the engineering profession offers to those without formal educational qualifications may be one of its strengths; it is also one of its weaknesses.

It is felt that a clerical or teaching post is the hallmark of the educated person, and as such requires no explanation to friends or relatives, while a job in a local industrial firm is too easily confused with that of a workman.

In the United States, career counselling has become a recognized profession; a large school will appoint a counsellor who advises the students both on career and on personal problems; the small school will often appoint a teacher-counsellor whose duties include both functions. Similarly in France a great deal of public money is spent on guidance and there is in each school a teacher who specializes in giving advice on careers. According to my enquiries few maintained grammar schools in this country have a careers master or mistress.

Industry itself can do much to help. The Federation of British Industries has inaugurated a careers card-index scheme. The members of this body list their requirements and opportunities on a standard card which is sent to headmasters and headmistresses. An extension of this would be valuable.

Boys who are at independent schools usually have very few serious career difficulties. In most cases their family background will be a professional one, and in consequence they will probably have a high level of information about many careers. The school will usually have a careers master, who will be able to provide precise details about occupations. There is, in addition, the Public Schools Appointments Bureau, whose main objects are to provide information for careers masters, to advise individual boys on their choice of career, and to place boys in industry, commerce, and the professions. There is, however, the fact that many professional parents dislike the idea of industrial careers for their children; they feel that such careers smell of the workshop.

It must be recognized that the opening of the doors of the grammar school in theory to all suitable children, has not solved all our educational problems; we must realize that many of these children need extra help and guidance in planning school courses and deciding on careers, particularly at a time of transition like the present. It is desirable that this help and guidance should be readily and universally available.

CHAPTER IV

HIGHER TECHNOLOGICAL EDUCATION

Institutions for higher technological education

In this country higher technological education is carried out in two main types of institution, the university and the technical college. For the purpose of this chapter we will define higher technological education as being education in the basic sciences, engineering, and technology, at undergraduate and post-graduate level.

During the past few years there has been a considerable amount of controversy about which type of institution should be expanded to deal with the increased demand for techno-logical education. There were many arguments in favour of each side. It was said that only the university could attract the best brains in the country, because of the prestige of a degree and of a university career; the technical colleges maintained that if they were allowed to develop in freedom, they could create their own prestige. Many people disliked the idea of the universities being flooded with potential technologists, and maintained that only the more academically and research-minded engineers should be trained in a university, and that men for the more practical jobs should enter the technical colleges. University engineers resented the imputation that they were not practical.

The Organization for European Economic Co-operation, in a report[1] on scientific research and training, said,

It is important in this context to distinguish between universities and technical colleges in the U.K. Universities are independent institutions, governed in accordance with the provisions of Royal Charters or Acts of Parliament. Technical colleges, generally speaking, are managed and financed by local education authorities, under the regulation of the Ministry of Education.

[1] *The Organization of Applied Research in Europe, the United States and Canada*, Vol. II: *Applied Research in Europe*, Organization for European Economic Co-operation, Paris, 1954.

In the field of technological education, university and technical college courses have hitherto been distinguished by the degree of concentration on academic study required of the student at some stage in the combined course. The university requires complete and continuous concentration on such study for at least three years, combined with only vacation experience in industry, and its students can have no industrial obligations or commitments which interfere with that concentration. Most technical college courses, on the other hand, are normally interwoven throughout with concurrent works practice and require only part-time attendance from students whose major commitment is full-time industrial employment. This practical distinction in the relation between academic study and works experience roughly corresponds with a distinction of principle between two aspects of technological education—the science and the art. In its aspect as a science it is concerned with general principles which are valid for every application; in its aspect as an art it is concerned with the special application of general principles to particular problems of production and utilization.

To the student, the essential difference between courses in a university and in a College of Advanced Technology is in the entrance qualifications demanded. The university sets definite matriculation standards; the college may take a weaker student and arrange for him to take preparatory and additional courses. In other words the colleges maintain an open-door policy, more like the American universities; the important thing is the maintenance of terminal standards. In addition the colleges are in existence to meet vocational needs; they will run specific courses on the request of outside bodies which is something that the university usually does not do.

Nevertheless, there is a certain overlapping of the function of the university and the technical college. Many universities now have highly specialized technological departments. At Leeds there are Departments of Coal Gas and Fuel Technology, Colour Chemistry and Dyeing, Leather Industries, Mining and Textile Industries; Birmingham has Malting, Brewing, Applied Biochemistry and Mining; and Sheffield has Fuel Technology, Glass Technology and Mining.

Recent history of higher technological education

The Percy Report

In 1944 the Minister of Education appointed a committee, under the chairmanship of Lord Eustace Percy, to consider the present and future position of higher technological education in England and Wales. The report of this committee (known as the Percy Report) was published in the following year, and has become a blueprint for the expansion of technological education. It explained logically the whole position, and stated that the crux of the matter was the complete co-operation of the industrialists and educators, and the realization that public spending and legislation would not be enough, since a change in public opinion was needed too.

Among other things, the Percy Committee discussed the roles of the university and technical college in technological education. They came to the conclusion that the training of scientists and engineers for teaching, and for research and development, should be the work of the university, and that of the technical assistants and craftsmen should be the responsibility of the technical college. It was agreed that between them they should share the task of educating the senior administrators and technically qualified managers of the future.

Technology is a science and an art. It was thought that the university selected and emphasized the science aspect, and the technical college the art aspect. However, criticism was made that this art aspect was being over-emphasized, and that the technical colleges had insufficient time to devote to courses in the fundamental sciences.

The Committee recommended new courses at the higher level in technical colleges, and that these courses should not be inferior to university courses, should require equal ability, and should prepare the student for advanced and post-graduate studies. Substantial periods of full-time work were envisaged for these courses and for this, new qualifications were recommended.

One of the most important recommendations was that a strictly limited number of colleges should be upgraded to advanced colleges, and should shed all their elementary work; the staff of these institutions should have salaries and working hours similar to those enjoyed by university staffs; and the colleges should receive a substantial amount of direct aid from the Ministry of Education.

Co-ordination of work in these and other colleges with university work was then discussed, and it was decided that Regional Advisory Councils and Regional Academic Boards were necessary. The former was to consist of representatives of industry, local education authorities, educationists and teachers, and the latter of academic heads of universities and technical colleges, and members of their teaching staff. On the national level a National Council of Technology was advised. This would not only co-ordinate all technological work, but would be responsible for 'recognizing' courses in colleges as adequate for the new technological qualification.

The suggestion of a new qualification became immediately controversial even within the Percy Committee itself. It was agreed that the colleges should in principle determine their own syllabuses and courses, and conduct their own examinations, and that the new National Council should under no circumstances act as an external examining body, but should approve courses, external examiners, staffing, and equipment. The dissension was over the title to be given to this new qualification. Some maintained that the equivalent to a degree necessitated a similarity of title, and suggested that Bachelor of Technology (B.Tech.) was appropriate. Others thought that the qualification, though equivalent to a degree, was essentially different from it, and should therefore receive a different title, such as a Diploma in Technology (Dip. Tech.).

It was felt that if a degree was awarded it might be regarded as a second-rate one for those who had been unable to obtain admission to a university; they recommended that the essential difference in the courses should be emphasized by a diploma given under State authority. Industrialists are interested in training, they argued, and would soon estimate the worth of a diploma, which would create its own prestige, and establish itself as a worthwhile qualification.

Those in favour of a B.Tech. pointed out once again that industry was not getting its fair share of national ability, and that consequently the new award must be of a kind to attract the most able schoolboys (and schoolgirls) in the country, and that this could only be achieved by making the qualification a degree. A degree is nationally recognized, both in the schools from which the recruits must come, and in the industrial and Government establishments which need the products of the new courses. It was felt that those who obtained the new award should be shown to have a qualification equivalent to that given to their fellows who had studied medicine, law, science, and the humanities. In addition, a degree would raise the status of schoolchildren in the secondary technical schools (which is still regarded as a very desirable aim), as the ultimate qualification to be obtained by both grammar- and technical-school pupils would be the same. It was also stated that the man who went overseas to work wanted the prestige of a British degree.

Both sides were agreed on the necessity for a higher research qualification analogous to the Ph.D.; D.Tech. was suggested. It was also decided that there should be a certificate for postgraduate study of one or more year's duration, in addition to research awards.

Lord Eustace Percy added to the Report a note on the disagreement over the new qualification. He said that there was no question of a conflict of interests between the university members of the Committee and the others. He personally thought that if the award was in every sense of university standard, then a university degree would be appropriate. However, the distinguishing mark of a degree was that it was awarded by a completely independent body; the major technical colleges were not as yet completely independent, although in time they might be raised to university status, for even university colleges have to serve a long apprenticeship. Lord Eustace considered that the best interim arrangement would be to award an Associateship of the Royal College of Technology at the graduating stage, and a Fellowship for post-graduate work.

The Committee also recommended State Bursaries and Scholarships for students from industry entering full-time or part-time courses at universities and technical colleges. They were anxious that the two types of institution should so arrange things that it would be easy to transfer from one to the other.

Most of the recommendations of the Percy Committee have in one form or another been adopted, but there is as yet very little provision for transfer from the technical college to the university, as the latter guards its rules and customs jealously.

The Barlow Report

The work and function of the universities themselves came under review in 1946 with the publication of the Barlow Report.[1] This report endorsed the recommendations of the Percy Committee, and expressed the hope that some university institutions might be developed from among the major technical colleges.

Some [technical colleges], situated in University Cities, might become the Faculties of Technology of the neighbouring University after a period in which standards had been worked out with the University on the basis of mutual acceptance of each other's teaching. Others, geographically remote from existing Universities, might qualify for independent university powers. . . . But the measures recommended by the Percy Committee for Technical Colleges will not absolve the Universities from their responsibility for training a high proportion of the nation's first-class technologists. We think, indeed, that the Universities should aim, by the provision of courses in the engineering sciences and full facilities for post-graduate research, to attract into technology a greatly increased number of students of outstanding ability. Certainly the expansion in the numbers of students in technology at the universities should not be less than that which we recommend in the case of pure science. In the course of their expansion and development we believe that both the universities and the selected colleges will have to provide training for qualifications such as chemical engineer and engineer-physicist, in addition to such existing schools as engineering and mechanical sciences.

Finally, in order to provide technologists of the highest possible quality, we think that urgent consideration should be given to the development of two or three Institutes of Technology, preferably in University Cities, whose aim should be to provide graduate and post-graduate courses and to conduct research of a standard at least equal to that demanded of candidates for doctorate degrees in the Universities.

The recommendation for which the Barlow Committee is remembered was that not only should the annual output of scientists and technologists be doubled, but so should the output of graduates in all Faculties (thereby retaining the existing balance between the humanities and the sciences).

. . . we attach very great importance to the atmosphere of an association of men and women which takes all knowledge as its province and in which

[1] *Scientific Manpower.* Cmd 6824, H.M.S.O., London, 1946.

all branches of learning flourish in harmony. Such an atmosphere has a great part to play in completing any student's education and preventing him from becoming a narrow and cloistered specialist. In particular would we deprecate any attempt to meet the increased demand for scientists and technologists at the expense of students of other subjects (even if, as is unlikely, the Universities could be persuaded to make such an attempt) or to give any preference to science students over arts students in such matters as military service.

Those who were concerned about the acute shortage of scientists and technologists and who realized how much more acute this shortage was to become, were somewhat alarmed by this recommendation. Many of them would have liked the universities to concentrate on producing what the community needed, and to realize that the old conception of a university, aloof from the world, had to be modified to meet changing conditions. However, the universities weathered the storm, and only a small change occurred in the proportion of those reading arts and science subjects.

Further reports

In 1950, the National Advisory Council on Education for Industry and Commerce[1] recommended radical improvements in the accommodation, equipment, and financing of technical colleges, and in the salaries and conditions of teachers employed. This was to allow the colleges to develop and to gain prestige. Inducements to encourage students to undertake courses in these colleges were considered, and it was decided that a suitable award was necessary. The old controversy about the nature of this award was revived. A suggestion that the London external degree would solve the problem was rejected as it was felt that it did not allow the Colleges freedom to develop their own courses. They came to the conclusion that an alternative national awarding body was required, and suggestions for this covered a very wide range.

(1) A Technological Grants Committee for Technical Colleges parallel to the University Grants Committee for universities. This would introduce complications owing to the responsibility of the Ministry of Education and local education authorities for the financing of technical colleges.

[1] *The Future Development of Higher Technological Education.* Report of National Advisory Council on Education for Industry and Commerce, H.M.S.O., London, 1950.

(2) An Association of Professional Institutions: we do not think that an association of professional institutions by itself would provide an adequate solution, although we agree that the institutions should participate fully in co-operation with other interests in a national body.

(3) An Association of Colleges or Departments of Technology in a Technological University. An association of colleges in a technological university would not be acceptable to the universities, and in any case we believe that the technical colleges should individually develop their own traditions and acquire a recognized prestige of their own.

(4) A Royal Council of Technology concerned only with courses and awards at the first award level. The objections to a Royal Council so limited are:

- (*a*) that post-graduate courses in technology already exist in technical colleges, and
- (*b*) that the national body, in addition to approving courses and making awards, might well be able to assist in promoting technological education in other ways.

(5) A Royal Institute, Society or College of Technology. We appreciate the objections of some professional institutions to the use of the term "Institute" or "Society", and we think that in view of the nature and functions of the body proposed, the name "Royal College of Technology" is the most appropriate that can be devised.

They recommended that this Royal College should

(1) approve suitable courses of advanced technology submitted by technical colleges under conditions appropriate to first and higher awards;

(2) approve the appointment of suitable external examiners to assist the colleges in setting and marking their own examinations.

The suggestions for the award were a degree; a certificate at the first level and a diploma at the second level; and associateship at the first, membership at the second, and a fellowship for higher distinction. The degree was dismissed because it would not receive the support of the universities, and also would not provide technological education with its own hallmark; the certificate and diploma were rejected because they did not suggest an award equivalent in status to university awards; so the third alternative (associateship, membership, and fellowship) was recommended as desirable.

The Parliamentary and Scientific Committee (an unofficial group of members of both Houses of Parliament and representatives of certain scientific and technical institutions) produced a memorandum[1] on the subject in 1954. They expressed concern about the scientific manpower position in this country

[1] *Memorandum on Higher Technological Education.* Parliamentary and Scientific Committee, July 1954.

compared with that in the United States. They were anxious that 'The arbitrary dictum of the Barlow Committee that the number of arts students should be doubled as well as the number of science students should now be abandoned.'

Sandwich courses were regarded by this Committee as worthy of development, and they advised that they should be confined to 'a limited number of technical colleges in the country where really adequate facilities could be provided.'

They recommended that a few colleges should be selected as Royal Chartered Colleges of Technology, to which entry would be either direct from school or by an Ordinary National Certificate.

The courses and examinations should be of such a nature as to exempt, at least in part, from the examinations of the professional institutions. The Higher National Certificate might then be adjusted so as to be more suitable for the technician.

Government plans

Finally in 1955 the Government announced its intention of setting up a National Council for Technological Awards. The Council was to approve courses in colleges as adequate for the new qualification which was to be a Diploma in Technology (Dip. Tech.), and it would not in any way dictate syllabuses, but would simply make sure that the content of the courses, the staffing, and the equipment, were of a suitably high level. This Council has now been set up under the chairmanship of Lord Hives.

In February 1956, the Government published a White Paper[1] on Technical Education, which gave details of future plans. The capacity of advanced courses in technical colleges was to be raised from 9,000 to 15,000 as soon as possible; in addition the numbers released by their employers for part-time courses during the day were to be doubled.

A five-year plan for expenditure was announced. Projects totalling £70,000,000 were to be started between the years 1956 and 1961, and these were estimated to require a further expenditure of £15,000,000 on equipment.

[1] *Technical Education*. Cmd. 9703, H.M.S.O., London, 1956.

These resources were to be concentrated mainly on a small number of colleges devoted to work at the higher levels. Nine or ten colleges were to be designated Colleges of Advanced Technology to undertake instruction at the highest levels. A number of other colleges were to be designated as regional colleges undertaking a good deal of advanced work. Efforts are to be made to provide the Advanced Colleges with hostels in order to encourage corporate community life.

As a recent report[1] noted:

The Diploma in Technology to be granted by the National Council for Technological Awards will be denoted by Dip. Tech. (Eng.) for engineering and by Dip. Tech. for other technologists and will be awarded in two honours classes and at a pass level. The minimum age of admission to recognised courses will normally be 18 and the standard of admission will be that of the General Certificate of Education, with two appropriate subjects at advanced level, or a comparable standard such as that of holders of good Ordinary National Certificates. Practical and academic training will be integrated in the courses recognized for the award. These will consist either of at least three years' full-time study, a major period of at least one year, to be completed by the end of the study course, or of a sandwich course covering at least four years' academic studies in a major technical college and including organized studies during the periods of practical training in industry.

The eight colleges provisionally designated as colleges of advanced technology in June 1956, are: the Birmingham College of Technology, the Bradford Technical College, the Cardiff College of Technology and Commerce, Loughborough College of Technology, the Royal Technical College, Salford, and, in London, the Battersea, Chelsea and Northampton Polytechnics. In the South West, Bristol College of Technology has been selected as a potential college of advanced technology and a tenth college will be chosen from those on the North-East Coast.

and

The expansion of advanced courses is being aided by a special higher rate of grant from central government funds, introduced in 1952, and a new national Diploma in Technology is being instituted. This will be awarded for the successful completion of courses at approved colleges of technology and these will be equivalent in standard to honours degree courses at a British university. The award will be made by the National Council for Technological Awards, an autonomous body set up by the Minister of Education in 1955 to approve the syllabuses, accommodation, qualifications of teachers and the examinations to be held in colleges, and to grant an award of national standing to students who follow approved courses and satisfy the examiners.

A report on sandwich courses by the National Advisory

[1] *Technological Education in Britain.* Central Office of Information Reference Pamphlets No. 21, London, 1957.

Council on Education for Industry and Commerce was reproduced as an appendix to the White Paper. Among other things, it noted:

> The National Advisory Council support the sandwich system of organization of course at all appropriate levels. They are, however, most strongly impressed by the opportunity which the system offers of developing schemes for training to professional level school leavers and other young people with ability to become professional engineers and technologists capable of filling responsible positions in industry. . . . The professional type of sandwich course should normally cover a period of 4 to 5 years for selected students and should be of such a standard that it may be expected to satisfy the requirements for the new technological award to be administered by the Council over which Lord Hives presides.

The new qualification for technologists

It may be seen that much of the thought which has been given to technological education during the past twelve years has been devoted to deciding on the names to be given to the new qualification and to the body which was to award it.

The present writer feels that Lord Eustace Percy, in his appendix to the report which bears his name, understood the problem fully when he pointed out that the hallmark of a British degree was that it had been awarded by a completely independent society, and that even university colleges had to serve a very long apprenticeship before they were allowed to award their own degrees. He felt that the new award could make its own prestige, and if the champions of the degree won their case, the new degree would tend to be regarded as an inferior one. It is unfortunately true that external degrees do not have the prestige of internal degrees. This may be because of undue snobbery on the part of those graduates fortunate enough to have spent three or four years as full-time students, and may have no bearing on the prestige of courses which will involve substantial periods of full-time work under what it is hoped will be conditions similar to those in a university. But the feeling about external degrees is nevertheless significant.

The new qualification will find its own level, which may be above, below, or on a par with university degrees in engineering. It may then happen that the advanced colleges will cease to want to award degrees and will prefer their own award. The German Dipl. Ing. is highly prized, and it can lead to the higher degree of Dr. Ing. (which is surely the answer to those who object that only a Bachelor's degree can lead to those of Master and Doctor). The qualification will be judged not by what it is called, but by the men (and women) who possess it.

Those who are concerned about the terminology are anxious that a good proportion of the most able children should be attracted to the colleges, so that the students on leaving will be such as to gain respect. As with all new schemes, this cannot happen at once, and a certain amount of patience is needed.

The new Dip. Tech. brings many difficulties in its wake: for example, the proposal to recognize certain courses in the smaller colleges as adequate. There is the distinct possibility that these smaller colleges might not be able to provide satisfactory training in the ancillary subjects; in consequence there will have to be a *de facto* if not *de jure* 'recognition' (i.e. approval) of both the college and of particular courses.

This difficulty will not arise in the larger colleges, but there is in place of this the fact that many of these colleges have their own Diploma or Associateship which they regard as being of more value than the Dip. Tech. (simply because of this difficulty about the smaller colleges).

The merit of the Dip. Tech. is in establishing a nationally recognized standard, but the problems to be faced by the Hives Committee should not be underestimated.

University expansion

There is also to be considerable expansion in the universities. In the academic year 1955–6, there were eighty-four thousand undergraduates, and it is hoped that this number will have increased to at least one hundred and six thousand by the mid-nineteen-sixties. About two thirds of the additional students will study science and technology. Many universities will be able to expand under this plan; the largest extensions will be at Imperial College, London.

It has been suggested that the universities are training all

C   A.S.M.

those who will benefit from a university education, and that no great increase in numbers is possible without the universities lowering their standards. However, as a White Paper stated:

Last year [1955] the number of eighteen year-olds in Britain was 640,000; in ten years time it will be about 850,000.

Even if the proportions receiving university education remained constant there would be a greater demand for university places; however we have seen that many able boys and girls leave school earlier than is desirable. If they can be encouraged to stay on, there will be a very large additional group of potential students.

The University Grants Committee in a recent report[1] outlined the reasoning which led it to recommend that Imperial College should be expanded as the main centre for technological education in Britain:

In announcing the provision to be made for recurrent grants for the 1952–7 quinquennium, the Chancellor of the Exchequer (the Rt. Hon. R. A. Butler, M.P.) said that in making some provision for development, he had in mind particularly the need for scientific and technological progress. Nevertheless the Government shortly decided that technological education needed a further stimulus, and on 10th June, 1952, we were invited to advise how best rapidly to build up at least one institution of university rank devoted predominantly to the teaching and study of the various forms of technology.

It would have been open to us on this reference to recommend the creation of a new "technological university" and there was a certain body of opinion which would have favoured this course. Such a proposition raised two questions, first, whether it would be preferable to create a new institution or to build up an existing one; secondly, whether technological education at the highest level should be given in an institution limited to technology or in a university in which a wide range of subjects is studied.

On the first issue we had no hesitation, at a time when development was a matter of urgency, in preferring to build up an existing organization. The staff required to plan and launch a new institution of this type would have had to be of the highest calibre, and their withdrawal from existing institutions would have affected their current output of scientists and technologists without creating any immediate compensating supply. The planning and creation of a new institution of this type would take a long time, and it would have been a number of years before the first graduates were forthcoming. Many more years must have elapsed before it could have reached its full stature, however liberally it had been financed. An institution is not great by having fine buildings and lavish equipment. Its greatness is derived from the quality and spirit of those who work there, and men of the

[1] *University Development*: Interim Report on the years 1952–1956. Cmnd. 79. University Grants Committee, H.M.S.O., London, 1957

quality desired will only be attracted to an institution of outstanding reputation. Reputation is a slow growth which cannot be forced. The reputation of institutions abroad, which has led to the desire for similar institutions here, has been the fruit of many years of achievement.

As regards the second issue, we should regard the isolation of an institution confined to a narrow range of subject as unfavourable to the highest attainment. This is the view which has been taken by a number of Committees which have been appointed by Government in recent years to consider the organization of higher education in other forms of applied science. As a result of the recommendations of these Committees extra-mural schools of medicine, dentistry, agriculture and veterinary science have been brought within existing universities. If these recommendations are right for the application of science to the practical problems of healing sickness and growing food, there is no reason why they should not be of equal validity for its application to the practical problems of industry. We considered, on evidence both from at home and overseas, that it was desirable, and indeed imperative, to keep applied science in the closest possible touch with the pure sciences, and we also attached importance to contact with the humanities, many of whose disciplines are becoming increasingly recognized as a necessary part of the education of the technologist.

It was decided that the building up of Imperial College would give the advantages of both a technological and a general university, because of the relationship of the College with the rest of the University of London.

In addition, the Committee recommended major developments at Glasgow, Manchester, Leeds, and Birmingham, and other developments at Bristol, Cambridge, and Sheffield.

It has recently been announced that in the new Winston Churchill College the emphasis will be on science and technology.

The main expansion in Imperial College will be in postgraduate work, mainly because of the many new technologies which have been developed recently. It is thought that it would be undesirable to have a primary degree in a subject like nuclear science, and that the correct way is a sound primary degree first (in this example, physics) and then a course in the particular technology.

Many students will work in industry between graduation and embarking on these post-graduate courses, and when released they are often financed by their firms for the necessary period.

Conversion courses for the Arts Sixth

One of the contributions of Imperial College has been its 'conversion' course for students who have specialized in arts subjects while at school; this preliminary year offers a special means of entry to the able non-scientist. Applicants who have reached a high standard in arts subjects will be admitted to this preliminary course; they are expected to reach normal entrance standards by the end of the year, and to be able to embark on the normal first-year course. Similar experiments have been tried in a few other universities.

General subjects for technologists

Closely related to this problem is that of teaching general subjects to undergraduates in technological faculties. It is argued that the student must be made aware of the wider issues both for his sake, and for the sake of his future employers. This is a controversial subject; many people argue that general education is the function of the schools.

In his inaugural lecture[1] to Imperial College, Dr. R. P. Linstead said:

> The most ardent advocate of a wider education for scientists and engineers would be displeased if our bridges collapsed, our electric light failed, our drinking water became polluted or our oysters became radioactive. With all this in mind I wish to take a stand in defence of the hard pressed undergraduates and to say that while the total length of the degree course remains the same it will not be possible to introduce non-scientific subjects to any extent into the formal curriculum.

This difficulty so far remains unsolved.

Management training

Another controversial subject of the present is the courses in management training. In an engineering concern, top management positions can rarely be filled satisfactorily by men trained solely in business administration, simply because so many of the decisions are engineering ones; the advocates of these courses will usually agree, but will argue that some form of management training for engineers is desirable so that the top engineers may see the wider implications of their decisions.

[1] *The Future of the Imperial College.* R. P. Linstead (Inaugural Address), London, 1955.

Such training is normal in the United States; it is included as part of the undergraduate curriculum in France; it is widely practised in Switzerland; and is gaining ground in other European countries. The Anglo-American Council on Productivity was impressed by the high regard which American industry has for graduates; this is largely because of their ability in management. In this country, work on industrial relations is being carried out, but it is still on a small scale.

It is to be hoped that training in this field will be given to all engineers in future. This may take place either in the universities or in the technical colleges; there is room for both in the industrial training of the future.

Teachers for technical colleges

So far, the technical colleges have been at a distinct disadvantage in recruiting teachers for subjects which are common to both types of institution. They can rarely offer conditions comparable to those in universities. Long teaching hours are usually required, with a good deal of evening work, and there is often little time for research or even for outside activities.

The colleges which have been upgraded to Colleges of Advanced Technology, or to regional colleges, are beginning to remedy this situation and are trying to offer good conditions to their staff. It is realized that this is a first essential to building up the reputation of the new Colleges.

The Willis Jackson Committee, in its report,[1] suggested that new avenues should be explored for technical teachers:

More use should be made of late entrants to the profession from industry, the Armed Forces, the Scientific Civil Service and Research Associations. The possibility of using more married women, and retired people from industry, should be investigated.

Technical colleges are allowed to give some recognition for previous industrial service, but within narrow limits. Unless these are widened there will be little inducement for people to enter teaching from other fields.

[1] *The Supply and Training of Teachers for Technical Colleges*, H.M.S.O., London, 1957.

The training of university engineers

There are two distinct methods of training university engineers; one is to teach fundamental ideas only, and leave the student to pick up the practical side in his first job; the other is to introduce students at an early stage to machinery and to methods which are in everyday use in industry, so that he will not be at a loss when he sees them on the shop floor.

It has been suggested that the more fundamental type of engineering training is well suited to the more able man, and that for the less able a more specialized course is suitable.

The London Polytechnics

Colleges which will occupy and have occupied a special place in the training of technologists are the London Polytechnics, which are unique in the technical training facilities of the country since they lack the regional affiliations of the technical colleges. Started as places of recreation for the poor, the Polytechnics now teach at university standard. (In some of them the students are internal students of the University of London, in others external.)

I paid a number of visits to the Polytechnics at an early stage in my investigations, and was impressed both by the high standard of work achieved and by the liberal outlook of their Principals. Most of them are financed by the London County Council; they have had a serious 'out-county' problem. Fees for students living within the L.C.C. area were of the order of £25 per annum (full time); for students outside, this was raised to between £280 and £320, which is the full cost of the course. In many cases the local authority would pay the difference in the two fees to the L.C.C., but if the authority was trying to establish its own centre for technological education it would normally refuse to make any such payment. The situation is complicated by the fact that all foreign and overseas students (including those from Scotland and Ireland) could attend at the reduced rates without any difficulty. A similar situation exists or did exist in technical colleges and in other locally-controlled institutions throughout the country; there have been recent efforts to correct this.

The National Colleges

A further type of institution is the National College. A specialized industry with a large number of small firms scattered over the country presents definite training problems. It would be extravagant to have a large number of centres for instruction, particularly if the equipment involved is expensive. To solve this problem National Colleges have been established; the first, for Horology, was set up in 1944 by Sir Stafford Cripps, with the intention of building up an export trade in watches. Since then there have been established Colleges for Foundry Technology; Rubber Technology; Heating, Ventilating and Fan Engineering; Food Technology; Leather Technology; and Aeronautics. Many of these colleges are housed in the London Polytechnics.

The main difficulty lies in the financing of students during these courses, since most Local Education Authorities think that they have done enough when the primary degree has been obtained. In many of the colleges the courses are run on a 'sandwich' basis, with the appropriate industry footing the bill.

Organization of technical education in Scotland

In Scotland, technical education has been developed along rather different lines. The population is concentrated around a very limited number of industrial centres, and in consequence a small number of large institutions have been set up; these have been followed by the local colleges.

These Central Institutions have governing bodies independent of local education authorities, and receive a direct grant from the Scottish Education Department; they also receive grants from industry. The work is of an exceptionally high quality, and reflects the great interest in education which we associate with Scotland.

CHAPTER V

TECHNICAL SCHOOLS AND COLLEGES: THE LOWER LEVELS OF TECHNOLOGICAL EDUCATION

The development of technical education

The craft apprenticeship system, which was standardized by the Elizabethan Statute of Artificers in 1562, is, as far as one can ascertain, the forerunner of technical education in Britain. The general idea behind this system (that a young man should learn his chosen craft on the job by watching and helping an experienced craftsman) is still the basis of craft training in this country.

The Industrial Revolution placed a definite strain on this method of training. The traditional simple operations were being replaced by more complicated ones using the new machinery. As the principles underlying these new machines had to be appreciated, if not understood, the craftsman had to be taught some elementary ideas of engineering. What was needed at this point was some attempt at both vocational and general education, but such training was not to come immediately. The Napoleonic Wars had left most of Western Europe, including France and Germany, in a disorganized state. England, compared with them, was in an advanced position of industrial production, and with little fear of competition the authorities saw no need to encourage schemes for technical education. In 1823 the Mechanics' Institutes were established as a result of voluntary enterprise, and by 1850 there were over six thousand institutes with a total membership of more than six hundred thousand.

These institutes were designed to give general, not technical, education to artisans, and it was felt that this would enable them to carry out their instructions more efficiently.

Meanwhile experiments in technical education were being carried out on an extensive scale on the Continent. At first the full significance of this was appreciated by few in this country, but with the Great Exhibition of 1851 when Continental goods of a high standard were exhibited, the industrial world at last realized the necessity for such an education. Britain still managed to win most of the prizes but the serious threat to her trade was recognized.

Thus in 1856 the Royal Society of Arts instituted a series of examinations in science subjects, and in 1859 the Department of Science and Art was also established to conduct examinations. In 1873, the craft examinations of the Royal Society of Arts began; in 1879 the City and Guilds of London Institute took over their work, and is still the main examining body in craft subjects.

The international exhibitions, which were so popular in the nineteenth century, seem to have been the main way in which a country's industrial prowess was measured, and there certainly seems to have been a great deal of prestige attached to the prizes. The result of Britain's failure to gain a large number of prizes at the exhibitions held in Paris in 1857 and 1878, was the appointing of a Royal Commission in 1881 'to inquire into the instruction of the industrial classes of certain foreign countries'. This commission recommended the provision of grammar schools, technical schools, and technical colleges, and in 1889 the Government set up authorities to work out schemes for technical and intermediate education.

There was at the same time a great deal of interest in the provision of general education for the children of the middle and lower classes, and many hoped that some means of combining general and vocational education could be found. In 1894 the Bryce Commission recommended that 'Technical education must be considered not as the rival of a liberal education but as a specialization of it.' It was intended that the new State secondary schools should give instruction in technical as well as general subjects.

However in 1905 the regulations for the secondary schools

insisted on a general education and in these schools was established the practice of following the curriculum of the public schools; a practice which was crystallized by the inauguration of the School Certificate Examination in 1917. These events marked the beginning of the division which has led to the two distinct types of school of the present day, the secondary grammar and the secondary technical.

To meet the need for technical education for schoolchildren, trade schools were established from about 1901 onwards and later they became the junior technical schools. These gave specialized training in a trade or industry, and catered for children between thirteen and sixteen.

By the nineteen-thirties it was realized that some order had to be imposed upon this system, largely because the provision for post-primary education varied so much from one area to the next. The Spens Report (1938) recommended that there should be three types of post-primary education, grammar, technical and modern; selection for these was to be made when the children were eleven years old.

It will be noted that the technical schools (called technical high schools in the Spens Report and secondary technical schools today) were now to recruit pupils at eleven and not at thirteen as previously; the aim of this was largely to give prestige to these schools. In the past, scholarship examinations for the grammar schools had been taken by the more able children at an age which varied from nine to twelve years; a second layer of ability was then selected at thirteen for the technical schools, and children in these schools were generally less intelligent than those in the grammar schools. It was hoped that the new system would select those children for whom the technical school would give the most suitable form of education.

One feature of the new system was its flexibility; the three streams were not to be regarded as completely separated, and transfers were to take place when appropriate. There had always been provision for this, but as one writer[1] said:

[1] *Technical Education and our Future*. T. J. Drakely, D.Sc., Ph.D., F.R.I.C., F.I.R.I. (North of England Education Conference, January 1946.)

In the twenty-five years' experience of the writer with secondary technical schools not one pupil per year has been sent from the grammar school, and even in those cases where the attempt has been made, the pupil has usually been either mentally defective or a nuisance in his grammar school.

The aim, as we have said, was complete flexibility; the whole climate of opinion in the immediate post-war period seems to have been a desire to remove the boundaries between one type of education and another. In its most extreme form this desire became one for comprehensive and multilateral schools, and for the abolition of the independent schools (or at least their conversion into State boarding schools for the maladjusted and underprivileged). On the other hand, many educationists were concerned with the maintenance of academic standards, and thought that there was little point in offering intellectually able children an academic education if that education were to lower its demands. This has been one of the most difficult problems of the past few years, and has unfortunately become politically contentious as well. We therefore find in some areas multilateral and comprehensive schools, and in others rigidly separated grammar and modern schools. This occurs according to the politics of the local authority.

Meanwhile the old Mechanics' Institutes were changing their original function as the spread of primary education had cut out much of the demand for general elementary instruction. In its place there grew up the desire and need for technical instruction for adolescents and adults. Many of the Institutes became technical colleges, and so began the practice of attending night-school which has always been such a feature of British industry.

Boys, who were apprenticed to skilled trades, started to attend appropriate evening courses during the period of their apprenticeship; the more ambitious ones continued even after the apprenticeship had finished with the intention of equipping themselves for jobs at a higher level. To meet the needs of this group new examinations were instituted. The City and Guilds of London Institute continued to administer those examinations with a craft basis; the more scientific subjects were tested at a higher level by the Ordinary and Higher National Certificate examinations. Preparation for these examinations took place in the technical colleges.

This situation continued for many years. During the Second World War, in addition to their normal courses, the colleges trained many people for war work, and worked long hours doing so.

The present situation in technical colleges

In 1953 when the Science and Industry Committee began its research, one of the first objects of its interest was the technical college. How had it fared since the war? What had been the effect of the Education Act? Had the increased opportunities for full-time education cut out some of the need for part-time technical education? Just what were the technical colleges doing?

The only way to answer these questions was to pay visits to a number of technical colleges, which I did in June 1955. I should like to express my gratitude to the Principals of these colleges for their help, by means of which it was possible to obtain not only an overall picture of their own colleges, but also an idea of technical education as a whole, its relation to industry, and its place in the world of today.

I was impressed by the very great variety in the colleges, and by their ability to adapt themselves to local conditions and requirements. Most of them were overcrowded but were going ahead rapidly with plans for expansion. There were also many complaints about staff shortages, and apparently for some technologies it was almost impossible to recruit teachers. However, the colleges were managing to continue their work.

We were very interested in the relations of the college with local firms. Many colleges had advisory committees composed of representatives from appropriate local industries; in others the industrialists were well represented on the Governing Boards or the appropriate sub-committees of the Local Education Authority. There are also Regional Advisory Councils, set up in 1947, which maintain liaison between the colleges and industry; and for the whole country a National Advisory Council on Education for Industry and Commerce exists.

A number of the principals found that their own personal contacts with leaders of local firms were of assistance to them when they were deciding on new courses, advising students on careers, or arranging for necessary equipment. There were some areas, notably the north-east of England, where relations were so cordial that local firms gave regularly to the colleges expensive equipment. Sandwich courses were being held in a number of colleges which were visited, and many employers made generous financial provisions for them. There are still, however, many employers who are reluctant to release an employee for half the year, and if the firm is small it may be almost impossible to do so.

Day-release is becoming more widespread, largely as a matter of necessity in a time of full employment, since young workers go where conditions are best. While day-release makes great demands on the colleges, it helps them as many of the teaching duties are shifted from the evening to the day, and also gives the staff more time to cover their subjects properly. It does, however, mean that a large full-time teaching staff is necessary, and that the colleges cannot depend as much as they did on evening lecturers (who are still very necessary).

The colleges carry out a number of full-time courses, although many people hold that this is not their main function, and that they exist essentially for the part-time education of those already employed.

Many of the colleges have been doing work of university standard, as has been discussed in Chapter IV. The present tendency is for the almost complete separation of this advanced work from the more elementary work, so that more prestige may be given to those institutions undertaking the advanced work. While this is very desirable, it is to be hoped that the process will not go too far, or else technical education will lose its flexibility. A student may attend an advanced course in one subject and a more elementary course in a subject in which he is weak, or may attend appropriate preparatory classes if he is not up to standard for the course which he wishes to join. This may still be possible when the two types of college are separated, but it may involve additional travelling and wastage of time if the classes are at different ends of the town, and this may result in the student giving up altogether. There is already a great deal of wastage in these evening classes; the object should be to minimize it. In addition, teachers for some technologies are in very short supply, and it might be more efficient to have one teacher to take both elementary and advanced classes.

The technical colleges are usually administered by the local Education Authority or one of its sub-committees. The form which this administration takes varies with the committee, some delegating almost complete authority to the Principal, and others keeping a close watch over the amount of chalk used.

At the lower levels the technical colleges seem to be doing a difficult job extremely well. They have to deal with students of widely varying academic attainment and abilities, and must devise courses and classes to suit everyone. Most of them are prepared to institute new courses at the request of local firms, sometimes at very short notice. Timetable difficulties are great, but somehow the job is done.

The technical school

At present many of the technical colleges also house the technical schools. This has been criticized by those who feel that the prestige of the technical school would be increased if it had its own buildings; nevertheless the sharing can promote efficiency in the use of teachers, particularly where the college undertakes little day work.

The prestige of the technical school is a vexed question. The Education Act envisaged the technical school as one of three equal types open to the eleven-year-old, and as a school to which a proportion of the most able children would go. In practice, some of the old traditions linger, and in many places the choice at eleven is between the grammar and the modern school. The examination which was to select the most appropriate school for each child has become an examination which some children pass (and are then allowed to enter the grammar school) and the remainder fail (and are then relegated to the modern school). There is then a separate examination taken by the so-called failures for a very limited number of places in the technical school. This is precisely what the Spens Committee wished to eliminate.

Therefore it is to be hoped that more technical schools will be built (and the present ones expanded) so that those children for whom technical education is suitable will be looked after, and that the selection of these children will be made at the same time as that for the grammar school. It is desirable that there should be increased facilities for general subjects in technical schools if not in technical colleges, and if any pupils from these schools wish to go to a university they must be able to develop interests similar to those of their fellow students from the grammar schools.

Technical training in other countries

So far, the problem has been stated and examined in terms of the present industrial training system, about which many authorities are beginning to have doubts, particularly with regard to apprenticeship. Many Continental countries have rejected traditional apprenticeship on the job, and instead train the young worker in special schools for a period which is generally shorter than the old apprenticeship period, but which gives a full-time training and a general education.

An increasing amount of apprenticeship training is given in the apprenticeship centres in France, and in the trade schools in Germany. The courses are shorter, but the apprentice is under constant instruction, and in addition has to reach a definite standard of skill to pass the examinations set during and at the end of the course.

This is something which could well be examined by educationists and Trades Unions, and it may be decided that it would be advantageous for us to have apprenticeship schools too.

However, we need not have too much fear of comparisons

with others, for rarely can an equivalent to the technical college be found on the Continent. Training schools abound and generally provide a much more thorough training than is given in this country, but are related to one particular grade. Few people have the opportunity to take part-time evening courses to improve their status while they earn their living at the same time.

CHAPTER VI

GRADUATES IN INDUSTRY

Industry's need for graduates

Industrial firms have always sought intelligent school-leavers, as it was felt that a young boy could be trained and moulded to meet the requirements of the firm. Graduates have not been so popular; they have often been considered to be too old and too unwilling to start at the bottom, and were also thought to be too unadaptable.

But now industry is beginning to find difficulty in recruiting competent schoolboys, and tends to blame the present education system for this. The older members of industry suggest that the boys of today are not so competent as they were in their youth. What is being overlooked here, is that the more competent boys are no longer in the labour market, since the present system of university scholarships and grants ensures that fewer people capable of benefiting from a higher education are now denied it. This results in a large proportion of the top intelligence group being no longer available for employment until they are graduates.

In addition to this, industry is becoming more and more aware of its need for trained scientists and technologists. Its demand from the university graduate is twofold; it needs his high level of intelligence and his academic training. Most firms complain that they are unable to obtain enough scientists and technologists. The small ones maintain that the 'giants' absorb all the available graduates; the older industries grumble that only the newer ones are attractive to the young. Some suggest that a firm must establish an expensive training scheme if it is to attract people, and that certain areas are more popular than others.

Enquiries made from University Appointments Boards

Just how true are all these allegations? How do graduates

D A.S.M.

decide what firm to enter? The only satisfactory way to answer these questions was to pay visits to some of the University Appointments Boards to discuss with the secretaries of these boards the whole problem, and to write to the remainder for their advice. I am most grateful for the ready help which I received from these busy people. The results form the basis of this chapter.

At the time when the enquiries were made (February 1956) the picture of graduate employment was distorted by the problem of National Service deferment,[1] when most graduates felt that the situation was in a state of flux, and that the following year's graduates might have to serve for a shorter period or not at all. There was therefore a rush for those jobs which offered deferment, as it was hoped that National Service would be avoided. This meant that many of the graduates were entering, for example, the aircraft industry with the intention of remaining there until they were twenty-six, and naturally many would remain there indefinitely. A small number were going abroad to avoid their National Service commitments, but new regulations which made those going overseas liable until they were thirty-six, were having their effect in preventing this.

The larger firms and graduates

There was almost general agreement that the bigger firms were able to recruit an inordinately large share of the graduates. This was partly attributed to the fact that most of the firms, who could offer deferment, were big ones, but there were other reasons too.

(i) The bigger firms can afford to send recruitment teams around all the universities, and to indulge in extensive advertising.

(ii) Big firms usually provide good training schemes. It is felt that this indicates that top management is interested in the use of graduates, who will in consequence not be frustrated and bored by routine work. In addition, engineers must serve a post-graduate apprenticeship of

[1] Since then the abolition of National Service has been announced.

two years if they are to qualify for membership of a professional institution.

(iii) University engineering and other societies often become familiar with the major firms through arranged visits, and hence graduates may go back to these firms when looking for employment.

(iv) Many graduates have no clear idea of what they want to do. If they enter a big firm it is usually possible to change to another department; this is rarely possible in a small firm.

(v) It is felt that the larger firms can afford to pay higher salaries, and can offer better prospects of promotion than the small firms, although some people feel that the personal elements may be submerged if the firm is too large.

(vi) The modernity and appeal of the product or activity is very important, and many of the latest developments are handled by big firms.

(vii) The appeal of research is paramount. Most students are conditioned by their professors to regard research as the most important thing in life, and consequently are keen to go to those firms with a good research reputation. This in general militates in favour of the large firms since few of the smaller ones can afford to provide good research facilities.

(viii) In a large firm there is a separation of functions so that the managerial structure is obvious; in the small firm one man may be doing three or four jobs and there may be few clear lines of responsibility, so that the graduate learns about administration in a more muddled way. Clearly organized training schemes are liked; in particular, the large firm will usually have an apprentice supervisor to co-ordinate all training.

Other factors affecting the graduate's choice of firm

Certain industries are unpopular; these include those which have so far been nationalized, iron and steel, cotton, and heavy electrical engineering (the emphasis is still on electronics). Most graduates are prepared to work anywhere in Britain, although there is a general preference for London and the South. Many are prepared to go abroad temporarily, but usually want to come back to settle down.

There is a feeling that the class of a degree is recognized in Government establishments, but not in industry, and that there is a more clearly defined status and greater prestige in Government employment. Against this, industry pays better.

In general, graduates wish to work for a firm where their own subject is of paramount importance, so that they will be in the main stream of interest and of promotion. Thus, for example, chemical firms find it difficult to recruit engineers.

Industry and the class of degree

However, the main question seems to be whether industry really knows what it wants from graduates. Some industrialists ask for as many first-class men as possible; others seek a large number of graduates who have been awarded second-class honours or a good pass degree, as they think they are more practical.

Why should it be assumed that the man with a first-class degree has neglected the wider issues, and consequently has a second- or a third-class mind? Why, conversely, do we assume that a second- or third-class degree indicates the captaincy of all the sports clubs, the presidency of the university debating society, political acumen, and the qualities which will rapidly lead to a seat on the Board? All of us can think of acquaintances for whom these assumptions seem to hold good; however, their universal truth has not been proved. It seems more reasonable that the class of a university degree does in some measure indicate the quality of the recipient's mind; that the man with a first-class honours degree has in the majority of cases a first-class mind (or at the very least the perseverance and intellectual stamina to study the undergraduate course more than adequately, and a good enough memory to reproduce it accurately).

Another common assumption, that the man with a first is

made for the research laboratory and is not suited to administration and the more general posts, is also questionable. The
first-class man is often the only one with the ability to carry out
research, and consequently he enters the research side of
the organization. The less able man may enter the sales force or
one of the more general departments where he will learn a great
deal about the firm and its policies, and may therefore be ready
for an administrative post long before his colleague in the
laboratory. And so the more able man may suffer because of
his own ability. This may occur in a slightly different way in
other firms. The more specialized posts in a design organization
are generally given to those with the ability to fill them; the less
able then gain the more general jobs in the main stream, and are
thus more in line for promotion.

This is not to deny the value of social and cultural activities
at the university; they are particularly valuable for scientists
and engineers, and do help to make the 'whole man'. Sometimes a brilliant student gains a poor degree because of his
preoccupation with other activities, but a poor degree need not
necessarily mean this state of affairs. In short, what has happened is that a reasonable allowance for the effect of outside
activities on the class of the degree has turned into an unreason-
able assumption that the universities get things the wrong way
round.

Another factor to be considered is that industry sees only a
proportion of those with first-class degrees. The graduates who
have achieved this standard by sheer brilliance and intellectual
attainment are often grasped firmly by their professors, and
start to tread the academic path, while those whose firsts
represent much hard work, and the turning of a blind eye to the
other attractions which the university has to offer, enter industry, and can give a totally false picture of the meaning of
their degrees. In fact, by holding on to the best of its graduates,
the university can do itself a great disservice in that a false im-
pression of its grading process and even of the quality of its
products may be obtained. This did not matter in the days when
graduates entered professions effectively controlled by other

graduates, but it is of importance now when graduates have to compete with non-graduates on equal terms in industry.

Industry and post-graduate work

Industry, too, is still doubtful about the value of post-graduate work. A recent report[1] stated:

Fifty-four engineering firms answered the question as to whether they preferred to recruit graduates
  (i) directly after their first degree,
  (ii) after a period of post-graduate instruction, or
  (iii) after a period of research.
Twenty-four of them preferred to recruit men immediately after their first degree, without any qualification; a further sixteen said that they normally preferred (i) but liked a few men with post-graduate or research experience for specialized posts, especially on the research side of the business; three firms preferred graduates who had done a post-graduate instructional course; and only one firm chose without qualification men who had done some post-graduate research. In addition to these, four firms answered. "It depends on the vacancy"; five firms had no preference; and one firm thought it depended on the degree taken. There was thus overwhelming support for recruitment at the first degree stage except for special research posts. Among the nationalized industries, the position was very similar, and post-graduate experience was only considered desirable in exceptional cases for research posts.

The commonest reason advanced for the preference for new recruits at the first degree stage was the matter of age. It is argued that a graduate who spends two extra years at the University on work which is generally held to be of doubtful value, and then two years on National Service, will not be ready to enter industry until he is at least twenty-five years old. This is beyond the age a man should be when he starts getting practical experience of industry, and delays too much the age at which he should be ready to assume effective command. A subsidiary reason advanced was that, once a man stays on at the University for a period of post-graduate study, he tends to stay in academic life (including teaching) and is less likely to seek a career in industry. A number of firms recognized the value of post-graduate instructional courses but suggested that these had greater value if they were postponed until the man had some years' experience in industry. It was suggested that the universities should ensure that the kind of post-graduate work they encouraged was not of a kind better done in industry.

Non-specialist graduates in industry

About a quarter of all graduates go into industry. Most of these are scientists and technologists, but there are also a

[1] Report on the Recruitment of Scientists and Engineers by the Engineering Industry Advisory Council on Scientific Policy, Committee on Scientific Manpower, H.M.S.O., London, 1955.

number who have read for degrees in either arts, law, or economics. Non-specialist graduates may be employed in welfare, personnel or secretarial jobs; they may be given management training or a short technical course and then be used in administrative or semi-technical jobs.

Such graduates can be of great value in administration, but they may be given a status and salary superior to that enjoyed by the scientists and technologists in the firm. This may lead to the belief that it is better to read arts than science, and a recent report[1] suggests that this is actually happening.

From the results of a sample survey, the following tables, showing salaries paid to graduates, after graduation and five years later, were produced. (It must be remembered that these salaries are out of date, and that in particular most new graduates now receive much larger salaries.)

STARTING SALARIES IN PRINCIPAL EMPLOYMENT GROUPS

First career employment (after graduation in 1949)	Starting salary (median)		
	Arts	Science	Technology
	£	£	£
Teaching	530	518	—*
Universities	490	500	—
Civil Service	455	470	463
Industry	444	501	434
Local Government Service	432	—	405
Commerce	395	—	—
ALL EMPLOYMENTS	464	494	433

SUBSEQUENT SALARIES IN THE PRINCIPAL EMPLOYMENT GROUPS

Employment in autumn 1954	Subsequent salary (median)		
	Arts	Science	Technology
	£	£	£
Industry	768	729	752
Civil Service	690	653	783
Commerce	689	—	—
Teaching	653	660	—
Universities	656	647	—
Local Government Service	628	—	709
ALL EMPLOYMENTS	654	684	741

* Less than 20 graduates.

It will be noted from the second table that industry was paying

[1] *Salaries of Graduates in Industry.* Planning, March 1957.

arts men more than either scientists or technologists. As is said in the report:

A salary policy that offers little advantage to scientists and no advantage to technologists over arts men at the outset of their careers, and then promotes some of the arts men to positions carrying higher salaries than those filled by any of the scientists and technologists is not well calculated to encourage men to read science and technology rather than history or languages or some other non-technical subject. Yet it is for a greater emphasis on science and technology at universities that industry has for many years been calling. Its salary policy, as it emerges from this survey, and as it affects the first few years in employment, does not appear to have given all the encouragement possible to the achievement of this goal.

Training schemes and effective utilization of scarce manpower

It has been said that graduates like some form of training scheme when they enter industry. This is to everyone's advantage, as it helps the graduate to find his feet, and also to be of more use.

Some employers think that the Appointments Board is presenting them with the finished product rather than with the raw material, and so there are difficulties. The new graduate may need training on the spot; he may need classes in a particular technology, or advanced short courses on his own subject, at the local technical college; or he may even need eventually a post-graduate course at his own or some other university.

It is also important that the graduates should be fitted into the general employment scheme of the firm so that there is no resentment on the part of other employees at what seems to them privileged treatment. For this reason training schemes should consist in doing rather than watching.

Industry is learning to utilize its graduates to better advantage. The introduction of analogue and digital computors has helped to save much routine work by mathematicians and scientists; however, the efficient use of such aids demands very highly trained staff, which may cause difficulty in some firms.

The shortage of trained people is being met by some firms, who are recruiting graduates from other European countries. This is as yet on a small scale only, and presents difficulties when the firm is engaged on secret or confidential work for the

Government. In addition, many firms help to produce their own graduates. The sandwich course is growing in popularity; it is an expensive form of training but can be very rewarding. In some firms outstanding boys are given a 'thick' sandwich course, and this comprises practical training followed by the entire university course, and then followed by a further period of practical training.

There may also be upgrading from lower forms of apprenticeship. The usual practice is that trade (or works) apprentices are recruited at about sixteen, engineering (or technician) apprentices with some G.C.E. 'O' level subjects at sixteen or seventeen, student apprentices ('A' level) at eighteen, and graduate apprentices on graduation. It is usually possible for the most able boys in each section to be upgraded to the next form of apprenticeship by means of theoretical training in the local technical college. It is worth emphasizing again that the essence of training in this country has always been its flexibility, so that everyone may find his own level. This valuable feature of preparation for British industry is often forgotten.

CHAPTER VII

SCIENTIFIC WOMANPOWER

The problem

Every week we read in the Press that more women scientists and technologists are needed. Industry is exhorted to employ them; headmistresses are reminded that science is an exacting discipline and so they need have no fears about encouraging their more able pupils to read scientific subjects; parents are advised that lucrative and satisfying careers are open to the scientifically trained woman.

But why are more women not in scientific occupations already? What sort of careers may they expect if they do enter industry? How many women have the ability to study science at an advanced level? What about the often expressed opinion that it is not worth while to give a woman a long and expensive training since she will only leave to marry at the end of it? Do parents and headmistresses consider that scientific careers are unfeminine and so encourage the more able girls to study arts subjects? Do girls' schools provide adequate facilities for the study of science subjects?

In an attempt to answer at least some of these questions, enquiries were addressed to headmistresses, to Youth Employment Offices, to industrial managements, and to leading members of professions in which women are well established. Recent literature on this subject has also been examined. It was soon obvious that the problem was a complex one. No one group of people can be held responsible for the situation of women being heavily outnumbered in the scientific fields, for it is an indication of the way society thinks.

Of the degrees awarded in scientific and technological subjects a very small proportion go to women. Why is this so?

In a recent article,[1] Mrs Constance Arregger, a practising engineer, wrote:

It is now no longer argued that women are incapable of technical work or that the female brain is not suited to logical scientific reasoning, or that staying power is lacking. There are about a dozen women Fellows of the Royal Society and a few women professors. Women have made good in medicine—itself a science. For almost forty years disqualification on the basis of sex has been officially and legally removed and girls have had the opportunity, in theory at least, to have higher education and to compete on an equal footing with men.

Why, then, are women scientists and technologists in so small a minority—and at a time when there is an outcry for more scientists and technologists? Is there a barrier of masculine prejudice which keeps them out of this field, or do women themselves not find it sufficiently interesting to want to enter?

And the Federation of British industries has issued this statement:[2]

Women have already proved their worth in such fields as chemistry, physics, microbiology and statistics. The value of their work in laboratories is well known, and to a lesser extent they are being employed in such fields of engineering as design, development and planning.

Yet the number of women employed in such jobs over industry as a whole is well below the desirable figure.

This is due to two major factors: the smallness of the output by schools, universities and technical colleges of women with the necessary background and qualifications, and the reluctance of employers to train women for positions of responsibility, especially in the fields of science and technology.

This reluctance is largely due to the limitations imposed by marriage. The problem therefore is the suitability of younger women for technical employment in industry on the one hand and older women in senior positions on the other.

Younger women can make an important contribution to relieving the immediate shortage of scientists. Many girls possessing the General Certificate of Education even at Ordinary Level can become excellent laboratory technicians.

Married women technologists, wishing to return to industry after an absence of some years, might be well suited for the important functions of training and supervision.

Undoubtedly such things could happen, but why are they not happening?

Educational problems

Let us consider first the difficulties arising in schools.

[1] *Why so few women scientists and technologists?* Constance E. Arregger. *The New Scientist*, January 3rd, 1957.
[2] *Industry and Technical Colleges.* The Federation of British Industries, London, 1956.

A discussion of the facilities and the opportunities for the study of science in girls' schools is given in Chapter III. We may recapitulate briefly. Many girls' schools are understaffed and under-equipped for the teaching of science. The Science Sixth Forms are often small, and it is impracticable to cover a wide range of scientific subjects. In some schools, girls cannot take any science subjects at all in the Lower School.

At this point one hears the argument that most girls prefer to study the humanities and have little scientific ability, and one would agree that in general the humanities are more popular. But what of the girls who do have the necessary ability and desire to study science? Are they given the opportunity to develop it? The Central Advisory Council for Education[1] has this to say:

... It is common knowledge that many parents attach more importance to their sons' education than to their daughters'. The idea is not dead that a good education is wasted on a girl because she will get married, and if a choice seems necessary between taking a boy or a girl away from school it is usually the girl who leaves. If the mother dies, falls ill or is overworked, a girl may be brought home to look after the family.

Some light is thrown on the respective attitudes of parents in different walks of life by a comparison of the figures shown for boys and for girls in table below.

LENGTH OF SCHOOL LIFE: BOYS COMPARED WITH GIRLS

Academic categories (grouped to show length of school life)	Father's Occupation									
	Professional & Managerial		Clerical		Skilled		Semi-Skilled		Unskilled	
	Boys	Girls	Boys	Girls	Boys	Girls	Boys	Girls	Boys	Girls
	%	%	%	%	%	%	%	%	%	%
Sixth-Form leavers	46·8	41·1	30·9	27·0	23·3	18·1	12·7	6·7	7·2	6·1
(Fifth-Form leavers)	46·0	52·5	61·0	57·5	60·4	59·1	62·6	59·6	55·0	51·4
(Pre-mature leavers)	7·1	6·4	8·2	15·5	16·4	22·9	24·7	33·7	37·8	42·5
TOTAL	100	100	100	100	100	100	100	100	100	100

[1] *Early Leaving*. A report of the Central Advisory Counil for Education. (England) Ministry of Education, H.M.S.O., London, 1954.

It will be seen that at Sixth Form level boys are found in the majority in all groups. Among the earliest leavers there is a marked preponderance of girls everywhere except in the professional and managerial group. This suggests a difference of social convention about the level of education necessary for girls and may indicate the critical stages in the school life of girls with different social backgrounds.

What is the actual magnitude of the wastage represented by these figures? It is difficult to give a complete answer, but some assessment can be made of Sixth-Form wastage.

The Early Leaving Report considers the group of pupils who were regarded by their schools as suitable for advanced courses either in Mathematics and Science or in other subjects. The results were tabulated as follows:

COMPARISON OF SCHOOL LIFE OF THOSE THOUGHT SUITABLE FOR ADVANCED COURSES IN MATHEMATICS AND SCIENCE AND IN OTHER SUBJECTS

Length of school life	Boys			Girls		
	Best suited for:		Total	Best suited for:		Total
	2 'A' Maths & Science	2 'A' other subjects		2 'A' Maths & Science	2 'A' other subjects	
Stayed long enough to take advanced course	574 (13·9%)	456 (11·1%)	1,030 (25·0%)	194 (4·6%)	517 (12·2%)	711 (16·8%)
Left too early to take advanced course	290 (7·0%)	211 (5·1%)	501 (12·1%)	134 (3·1%)	355 (8·5%)	489 (11·5%)
TOTAL	864 (20·9%)	667 (16·2%)	1,531 (37·1%)	328 (7·7%)	872 (20·7%)	1,200 (28·3%)

This sample represents about 10 per cent of the whole annual intake into grammar schools. It may be seen that while some 3,380 girls were thought suitable for advanced work in Mathematics and Science, only about 1,940 girls completed such courses (and in fact, almost 5,000 girls who were considered suited to advanced work of any kind left school without completing appropriate courses). The Early Leaving Report estimates that most of these girls subsequently took up occupations or vocational courses of too low an intellectual level. The wastage lower down the school is serious, but it is felt that the loss of potential sixth formers is more important, and that efforts to solve this problem should have a beneficial effect throughout the school.

It will be noted that the proportion of girls thought suitable for advanced courses in Mathematics and Science is 7·7 per cent, which is not high, even when allowance is made for the fact that many girls may not have had the opportunity to show any ability in scientific subjects.

Engineering and scientific training and opportunities for girls

Consider now the girl who has overcome the initial obstacles. What lies ahead if she wishes to become an engineer or scientist?

The engineer

The Women's Engineering Society is reasonably hopeful about the future. In their handbook[1] Miss Verena Holmes warns those girls who wish to enter the engineering profession, that entry for them would not be so easy as it is for boys, and suggests that they should gain formal qualifications wherever possible. She emphasizes that theoretical and practical work are essential to the engineer, and while the former may be obtained in the universities and technical colleges, the latter is usually best when acquired in industry. For a girl it is more difficult to gain practical training than her counterpart. The Women's Engineering Society, which keeps a list of firms prepared to accept girls as apprentices, will, if necessary, approach firms on behalf of those girls who are unable to find suitable openings, and so ensure consideration of the case at a high level. When a girl becomes an apprentice it is advisable that she insists on the apprenticeship being a formal one and that she receives exactly the same course as a boy would. It is pointed out, however, that comparatively few engineering firms will accept girls as apprentices; even if they do, apprenticeship normally starts at about sixteen years of age. The would-be engineer will be lucky if she finds a suitable opening near her home, and many parents would be reluctant to let her live away from home when she is so young.

[1] *Engineering Training for Women.* Verena Holmes, B.Sc. (Eng.), M.I.Mech.E. Women's Engineering Society, London, 1955.

Sandwich courses are recommended, particularly college-based ones, as the student's industrial experience is arranged for her. Entrants to these courses are usually between seventeen or eighteen years old, and since the college will often have its own hostel, the parents are more ready to part with their daughters.

The would-be engineer is warned that her chances of making a career on the production side are slight, as a firm with males predominating will rarely appoint a woman as works manager or foreman; she will however find employment on the research and design side. There is, however, a greater chance of the woman entering the newer branches of engineering (Aeronautics, Electrical and Electronic Engineering, Heating and Ventilating), than the older branches (Marine or Locomotive Engineering, Naval Architecture, or Civil Engineering).

The scientist

A girl who wishes to read science (as opposed to engineering) at a university normally finds the path easier. After graduation she can find employment on the research side of industry, in technical information and library services, in Government departments and research organizations, or in teaching.

If she does not wish to go to a university she will probably find it very difficult to obtain employment other than as a laboratory technician. Even the most enlightened firms have only about one per cent of women in their training schemes for school-leavers with passes in scientific subjects at G.C.E. 'A' or 'O' level. This is generally attributed to a shortage of suitable applicants, which is a valid reason; it is suspected that higher standards are applied to girls than are to boys. Some firms complain, however, that even when they do advertise for women to enter training schemes there are few replies. The schools are largely to blame for this, but even so it is felt that, in this respect, many firms do not realize the advantages of publicity. An advertisement is not enough; direct contact with schools and pupils, talks, visits to works, and general advice, are all needed.

In many firms the sole occupation open to girls is that of laboratory technician. These posts, while often requiring a high level of attainment in scientific subjects, offer a very low reward. (I came across a young female technician, of good general education, who had transferred to the clerical side because the salary was higher, and because there was a recognized promotion ladder for clerks, which was lacking in the laboratory.)

The new magazine *Technology* has been investigating the employment of women scientists and technologists. It was found that most firms were very reluctant to give definite information about the subject. The general answer was that there were no barriers, but that publicity was undesirable. I am left with the strong suspicion that there is still a definite prejudice against women scientists and technologists, particularly where expensive training schemes are involved. However, few people have the courage to come into the open and say so for fear of being thought old-fashioned and unenlightened. This is surprising since the prejudice is often justified. No firm wants to spend several hundred pounds on training a girl who may promptly leave to get married.

Women at work: past and present

We have seen that there are many ways in which wastage occurs, and the prevention will need the efforts of industry, schools and parents. But it is meaningless to consider these changes in isolation; the social background against which the changes are to take place must be considered too.

When the supply of womanpower for any profession is under consideration, one of the first questions to be raised is that of the so-called wastage through marriage. Employers are naturally reluctant to admit girls to expensive training schemes when it is possible that they will receive little return for their investment. It can be argued that not all women marry, and that even those who do usually work for some time before and after marriage. Nevertheless, the problem of how much training to give remains.

Related to this, is the complaint that women are not career-minded. The unmarried woman is so because she intends to marry and leave; the married woman because she regards her job as even more temporary. It is alleged that this results in women adopting a casual attitude to their work, and so they are frequently absent and often careless. These charges cannot be completely denied, but are they entirely true?

Women at work in the past

For a fuller understanding of this problem, it is necessary to consider some of the history of woman's work. Prior to the Industrial Revolution, women were an integral part of the family working unit, and there was no conflict between family responsibilities and work. 'Under pre-industrial conditions, labour and leisure were not as definitely separated as they are now. Children were soothed with fairly tales while hands were busy on the loom.'[1]

Then when the work was taken from the house to the factory, women and children followed it; it took several decades of legislation to remove the evil effects of this step. The memories of the period influenced the social history of the nineteenth and twentieth centuries, and were largely responsible for the tradition that the only married women who worked, were those whose husbands could not afford to keep them.

The era of the Suffragettes came and went, and the doors of most professions were opened to women. Still it was the single woman who became the pioneer in a man's world, and she had often to risk gaining the labels 'unfeminine' and 'career woman'. 'To this day the term has such an unpleasant connotation for many people that professional women often hasten to assure you that they are not "career women".'[2] The career woman of those days usually had to resign herself to spinsterhood.

Throughout the Second World War, married women were forced to enter the labour market. Marriage was no bar to conscription for some kinds of war service, although women with young children were exempted. However, either from

[1] *Woman's Two Roles.* (page 30) Alva Myrdal and Viola Klein. Routledge and Kegan Paul, London, 1956.
[2] Myrdal and Klein, op. cit.

feelings of duty or thoughts of financial reward, many mothers placed their children in day nurseries and began to work. At the end of the war, many of these women left paid employment, though a surprisingly large number continued.

The new generation which was then growing up saw the conventional ideas of man's work and woman's work brushed aside. It was to be expected that this generation of young women would try to consolidate the gains of their mothers' generation; but there were opposing forces. During the war, many families had become unstable because of the absence of the father and the partial absence of the mother. Generally it was hoped that the presence of the mother in the home would help to restore stability; and that the children would be better cared for and less likely to get into mischief.

This was not all; the psychiatrists, basing their arguments on years of research, said that when a mother was away from home the child's mental as well as his physical well-being suffered. Women, and in particular professional women, applied to themselves and to their plans these new high standards of motherhood, and decided that it would be necessary to stay at home while the children were small.

It must be remembered that it was a comparatively new development for middle-class women to look after their children themselves; up to 1914 there had always been an abundant supply of women to look after other women's children. Once women were able to enter the professions the traditional props in the home (the nanny or nursemaid) began to dwindle in number. At the same time domestic workers became more and more scarce and more and more expensive as other work, which was better paid, became available.

Women at work today

A significant feature of the present dilemma for the young mother is the weakening of the bonds linking the basic family unit of parents and children with the larger tribal group of grandparents and relations. In a highly industrialized society, the younger members of the group often move to towns at a great distance from their families, and so there is generally no obvious substitute for mother close at hand. A report of the World Health Organization makes this point after showing how all recent investigations indicate that for proper mental and physical development a child needs the care of the same person between birth and three (possibly five) years of age. A paid substitute may be employed, but it is rare that a mother can be sure of three or five years service. The age of the nanny has almost passed.

Official opinion is against the working mother:

It is generally accepted that the employment of mothers with young children is at best a necessary evil and to be discouraged. This opinion is upheld by the Ministry of Labour, the Trades Union Congress, teachers, Women's Institutes, nurses, social workers and the great majority of employers. (In many cases, reductions have been made in the number of day nurseries and factory nurseries which alone made work possible for many mothers.)[1]

Day nurseries and nursery schools may be the partial answer, but once more expert opinion is against them. There are practical difficulties too. When a woman leaves her home to work, another must take her place if the children are not to suffer. A child with a cold is not wanted at the nursery school, nor is the child who has come in contact with a contagious disease which he has not contracted.

A responsible and conscientious mother of young children who is employed outside the home encounters many difficulties. There is the heavy cost of adequate domestic and child-minding arrangements; the net financial gain is smaller than that of the childless woman; and there is the emotional strain of working and raising a family at the same time. These difficulties are only outweighed when the interest in a career is overwhelming and the dislike of domestic duties is great.

The old order in which the husband kept his wife at home has passed away; in its place has come the new order in which women decide that once they have produced children they are indispensable in the home. The new bonds are of their own making.

The young woman of today continues work after marriage

[1] Married Women in Industry. E. M. Harris. Institute of Personnel Management, London, 1954.

as a matter of course; her reasons are often a mixture of financial gain, enjoyment of outside work, dislike of housework, and the fact that it is now regarded as somewhat abnormal and unenterprising to leave work on marriage. The first pregnancy, however, will terminate outside employment, the exact point of departure being determined by the employer, the doctor, and the employee.

For many women the conflicts we have been discussing will never arise; they will welcome the opportunity to devote their days to child care. However, even those who would like to continue working are aware that having produced children it is their duty to stay with them. The new mother will stay at home, at least during her child's pre-school years. This period will vary from family to family.

The older woman at work

From an economic point of view, it is desirable that women should return to work, particularly if it is professional work, once their children are old enough not to need them full-time. One feels that housework alone is not a full-time occupation.

But at what age do children no longer need a mother in full-time attendance in the home? Few people would deny that the over-sixteens do not need a mother's full-time care; we have argued that the under-fives do. But what about the five to sixteen year olds?

Magistrates in juvenile courts have railed against the mother-at-work, and in many of the cases before them, they have been justified. What has often been ignored is that the outside employment of the mother need not have been the crux of the matter; she may simply be incapable of controlling the child under any circumstances. This situation is different from that of the highly-trained and conscientious mother, who works only during the hours at which her adolescent children are at school, or who makes adequate arrangements for their care until she arrives home. For many children the effect may be beneficial; an increase of self-confidence and general capability may result.

What are the difficulties which a woman will face on returning to paid employment? Should she return to her profession or would she be wiser to enter another field? During the years of raising a family she may not have been able to keep up to date with her subject, but she will probably have done some reading, and should have remained mentally alert. She will probably find herself, somewhere between her fortieth and fiftieth birthdays, with an adolescent family and insufficient to keep her fully occupied. A generation ago she would have taken up social work, but this has now become professionalized, and there is little room for the well-meaning but untrained amateur. The most desirable course does seem to be a return to the field in which she has been trained.

However, while she may have kept reasonably up to date, her professional skills and attainments have not advanced at all. During the time that she has been away, the men of her generation have been advancing rapidly in their careers, and gaining their most valuable experience; the gap so created can rarely be closed. But the woman will have become used to authority in her own family, and so would find it difficult to settle down in a subordinate position; at the same time she would not have sufficient experience for a managerial post.

One can see certain obvious jobs for her; she would make an excellent supervisor for a group of young girls carrying out work of a routine nature. This would of course put her out of the main stream of promotion, but that is something which she would have to accept as inevitable.

This re-starting of a career for the mother has not yet become widespread; this is mainly because today the woman of forty has rarely had professional training, and in consequence cannot find what she and her family would consider a suitable job. Social snobbery tends to be important in this age group, and the woman who takes an unskilled job may find that her neighbours will not only look down on her, but will also speculate about her husband's financial position. Though there have been marked social changes, the idea that a woman should always be supported by her husband still exists. This situation is changing, however; most young women of today receive training of some kind, and should be able to find appropriate employment in later life.

The influx of a large number of women in their forties into a firm will inevitably cause some administrative difficulties. Questions of superannuation and insurance will arise; these are only administrative difficulties and not fundamental ones, and a satisfactory solution can probably be found.

Economic factors

There are many married women for whom no choice is possible; the reasons for which they work are primarily economic. In the lower income groups this may occur under any set of circumstances; for women who have received some form of advanced training, there are usually special circumstances such as widowhood, the illness or incapacity of the husband, or a desire to give children an expensive traditional education.

There is, in addition, the growing custom of working until the birth of the first child, for reasons which are generally economic, and usually it is the cost of establishing a home. Many experts on marital problems deplore this trend; they dislike the fact that the starting of a family may be delayed too long; they fear that the couple may become used to two salaries for two people, and have difficulties when it becomes one for three.

There are dangers that an inflated standard of living may be enjoyed for a time, with the consequent let down later. Rowntree and Lavers, in their study[1] of 1,278 married women (of whom almost 60 per cent had at least one child under fifteen) at work in York, found that while 441 gave as their reason for working 'to make ends meet', only 117 were in fact saving their families from poverty (on a scientifically constructed poverty line). (It is worth noting, from the same report, that 10 per cent of the married women in York whose husbands were in full employment, had paid work; in a similar survey[2] carried out by Rowntree in 1936, this figure was $3\cdot2$ per cent.)

[1] *Poverty and the Welfare State*. B. Seebohm Rowntree and G. R. Lavers. Longmans, 1951.
[2] *Poverty and Progress*. B. S. Rowntree. Longmans, 1941.

When considering the professional family, it must be remembered that if the normal standard of living is to be maintained, the salary of the wife will not be all profit. Her absence from the home leads to increased bills for food, laundry, clothing, meals out, domestic and nursing help, and personal items. In addition, the aggregation of the salaries of husband and wife for tax purposes may remove a lot of the profit. If the woman tries to avoid these increased bills and to run her home herself as efficiently as if she were in it all day, she will probably become so tired and run down that she will be unable to do her job properly.

Feminine professions

Two professions which women have entered in large numbers are nursing and teaching, which have always been regarded by parents, headmistresses, and the girls themselves, as particularly suitable since working with people is involved. (This is supposed to be something at which women are good.) But both require a rather long period of training, and the arguments about wastage must therefore apply to them; therefore I decided that it would be desirable to see what was happening in these two fields. I must express my gratitude for the very ready help which was given to me by all the authorities whom I approached.

Nursing

I found that in nursing the wastage is extremely high. Quite apart from the 15 per cent of student nurses who are rejected during the course because of an insufficient educational background, or because of the lack of the necessary personal qualities, a very high proportion marry shortly after the completion of their training, if not before.

What is the financial loss which this causes to the community? It proved impossible to make even a rough estimate; the actual cost of training a nurse is unknown, for the position is complicated by the fact that student nurses provide services for the hospital. At one time, the nurse in training was regarded as a paid employee, but now the official position is that she is a student, and so receives a grant, not a salary. The training cost, which includes costs of administration, nurses' homes, sister tutors' salaries, etc., is thought to be very high. And then one of the main results is the final product proves to be exceedingly marriageable.

Nevertheless, nurses are essential; the shortage is so acute that the wastage must be tolerated, and more help brought in at all cost. It has been found necessary to set up grades such as assistant nurse and nursing assistant to which are recruited girls, who might have difficulty in passing nursing examinations in the more academic subjects, but who have the necessary personal qualities and practical ability. This shows an awareness of the need for flexibility in a profession where there is a shortage of trained people. It could be taken as a guide and lead to industry.

Many women return to nursing after marriage, but it is difficult to fit them into a hospital staff which must provide a twenty-four-hour service. Married nurses naturally dislike evening and week-end duties, and yet it is essential that they should do their share of them, or else it will cause bad feeling among the rest of the staff. A possible occupation for the married nurse is Health Visiting, for which she can be based in her own home, and, within reason, work hours to suit herself.

In spite of all the difficulties, the Ministry of Health and the hospital authorities are prepared to go to great trouble to maintain this supply of essential womanpower.

Teaching

The picture is somewhat different in teaching; here, the pre-marriage period of work may be much shorter, since student teachers rarely provide substantial services during their training period. This is offset by the ease with which teaching duties may be combined with marriage. I am not minimizing the work involved in teaching; several hours of preparation are undoubtedly needed. It is, however, a job with a five-day week and little evening work, and so can fit in with a husband's working hours. Even when children arrive, part-time work is still possible (and teaching is one of the very few professions in which part-time work is available).

There are some difficulties. Advanced work of all kinds demands a great deal of reading, so that Sixth-Form work cannot be classified with general teaching lower down the school. This is particularly so with science teaching. It is thus quite common for a married woman teacher to decide to work in a secondary modern rather than in a grammar school, since little preparation is needed; a further inducement is that there are fewer of the extra-curricular duties which in some grammar schools may take a great deal of a teacher's free time. This may be to some extent a waste of highly trained womanpower, but it cannot altogether be deplored, as it is helping the secondary modern school to obtain well-trained staff, and should in the long run help to relieve some of the pressure on the grammar school. It is a perfect example of the compromise which is necessary if the married woman is to fulfil her duties both to her family and to the community. But, nevertheless, the teaching profession still has to depend mainly on the unmarried woman.

Lessons from these examples

What is to be learnt from these examples? First, in both these fields the shortages are great, and so married women are employed. Second, nurses provide very substantial services to the hospital during their training period, and are paid at a very low rate; they are essential to the running of the hospital services, and are more popular (and are paid less) than men. Third, married women cannot be easily assimilated into a twenty-four-hour hospital service, but are useful in such fields as Health Visiting, where they are home-based. Fourth, teachers are especially fortunate in that they can often find posts whose hours of work enable them to fit in their other commitments.

Women in the medical profession

The medical profession has for some time been complaining about the wastage of women doctors. This is a profession which, in spite of the long and uncertain hours of work, would seem ideally suited to a combination with marriage and motherhood, for it can be home-based, and the financial rewards are sufficiently large to enable the woman doctor to employ good nursing and domestic help. In spite of this the wastage is great, doubtless because many women feel that they cannot fulfil the exacting demands of this profession and at the same time live up to their own ideas of motherhood.

But the medical schools are overcrowded, and one may in consequence expect a reaction against this wasted training. Often a woman's professional life is shorter than her training period. It would seem that there is a possibility that the medical schools will become reluctant to admit too many women, and will almost certainly be highly selective. If the medical profession begins to discriminate against women, it is to be expected that industry will do so in an even more marked fashion.

Women doctors may argue that their training is not wasted, in that it enables them to become better wives, mothers and people. But a desirable by-product does not always justify the breakdown of the main production line. A similar argument may be applied to most forms of higher education. The answer seems to be that while the general education and development received is not wasted, the professional training is, since the professional skills acquired are neither used, nor conserved nor increased throughout the whole working life. The medical profession may make some slight allowance for the general benefits received, and the general good to the community of medical training; industry cannot be expected to rejoice because the mothers of tomorrow will think in a scientific way. Consequently, the murmurs of unrest among the doctors will find an echo in industry.

The woman in industry

What of the woman in industry? At what sort of career does she aim?

She will complain that when she is competing with a man for promotion, she must be very much more efficient and very much better qualified than he is in order to get the job. This is easy to believe and to understand. If the woman is young and unmarried, top management will decide that she may not be with them long; if she is married and childless they will be in almost daily expectation of losing her; if she already has children they will watch for signs that things are too much for her, and will wonder what would happen in the case of family illness or loss of domestic help.

All these arguments are quite valid, and there is little point in opposing them. The situation thus created must be quite infuriating to the occasional single woman who will spend her whole life at her job; she feels justified in demanding equal opportunities. There are difficulties even here; at what point does one decide that a woman is likely to remain single? Few people nowadays would consider that a woman in her twenties who was unmarried was likely to remain so. But what of the woman of thirty? And what of the fact that the man who is going to reach the top has already started on his way up by thirty? Will the woman ever catch up? Questions like these must continually vex the woman who is determined to make a career, and must often have the undesirable effect of making her behave in a somewhat belligerent manner, through feeling that she is a pioneer, and that the age of the Suffragettes is not quite over. While this attitude persists women have little hope of penetrating to many management positions. But, in the younger age groups, males are beginning to outnumber females, and in consequence fewer women will remain unmarried in future. The old idea of marriage versus career has gone; the young woman of today wants both, but will generally regard marriage as the more important. Employers must therefore take this into consideration when employing or training women.

Some general observations

Adjustments necessary

Perhaps it would be wise for headmistresses to help to develop some spirit of humility in their pupils; not with any idea of making them feel an inferior species, but enabling them to realize that in the world of industry they may be regarded as second-class citizens. If they are prepared to accept this, and to co-operate with others on those terms, they will not only find life easier and more pleasant, but will also be more readily accepted by employers. This may not be an easy pill for older women to swallow; younger ones will probably find it more palatable, and will welcome the more pleasant relationships arising from this attitude.

Comparisons with Russia

Comparisons with Russia are constantly made: we hear of their vast armies of women scientists, technologists and doctors, and of crêches and social services designed for the mother at work. These comparisons always seem somewhat pointless, as we are referring to two quite different forms of society. As we have seen in this country, we have developed the cult of the family and of maternal care; we would regard the Russian scheme of day nurseries as quite wrong. We must develop our own training within the framework of our own society, removing only those props which we are sure are undesirable.

Is science unfeminine?

To return to our discussion of science for women; why is it considered unfeminine? Mrs Constance Arregger lays the blame on parents and the toy cupboard;[1]

Could we not make science equally interesting to girls and boys at an early age—even very early?

Is there any reason why girls are given dolls and domestic toys where boys are given mechanical toys—except that parents arrange it that way?

Is it fundamentally any more feminine at the age of five to stick a needle into a piece of cloth than to hammer a nail into a piece of wood?

I realise that these suggestions may be premature. Perhaps the present generation of parents will find it difficult to treat their small sons and daughters as equally receptive beings, and it will have to remain for the next generation of more scientifically-minded parents to arrange a new mental climate for the very young.

There may be something in this. There is, however, the undeniable fact that while small girls will happily make mud pies,

[1] Constance Arregger, op. cit.

the older girl is rarely so fond of getting dirty. An occupation such as engineering which may mean extreme dirtiness at times is not really attractive to women. Prejudice there still is, but is it really the monster we have been led to believe?

CHAPTER VIII

PARTICULAR SHORTAGES

The principal shortages

As we have seen, there is a general shortage of scientifically trained people. This shortage is not, however, spread evenly over the whole field of scientists and technologists, but is felt very acutely in some branches of science and in some occupations, while it passes almost unnoticed in others.

One singularly acute shortage which springs to mind immediately is that of science teachers, for quite apart from the actual magnitude of the shortage, the effects are worrying. It may be a platitude to say that the scientists of tomorrow depend on the science teachers of today; it is none the less true.

Draughtsmen are in short supply, as also are certain laboratory technicians and chemical engineers. In this chapter some possible reasons for these particular shortages will be examined.

Science teachers

By far the most important shortage is that of science teachers; one hears on all sides complaints that a ridiculously small proportion of science graduates are entering the teaching profession, and that few of these have good degrees. This is serious, for in the schools quality is more important than quantity; since the size of the staff is usually fixed, quality is all-important. If science teaching is poor, children will become reluctant to take science classes.

Part of the shortage may be put down simply to the overall shortage of scientifically trained people, but that is not the whole story. Enquiries from University Appointments Boards confirm that only a very small proportion of new graduates intend to take up teaching as a career.

But what proportion of schoolteachers should there be? It may be that the annual intake needed is only a small one. To find out just what was happening in the schools, two surveys were undertaken. The first consisted of a series of visits to schools in Northern Ireland; the second of a postal questionnaire which was sent to 332 public and grammar schools in Great Britain (see Appendix 1).

It was soon obvious that the position in Northern Ireland was not too serious. This was so as there are fewer scientific industries to absorb the supply of scientists, and many young graduates wish to stay in the Province for family and personal reasons. Schools in Belfast had little or no difficulty in filling science vacancies, and could still afford to stipulate the class of degree required; country schools often had difficulty in finding someone who was regarded as suitable, but usually filled a vacancy with an appropriately qualified graduate. The replies from schools in Great Britain revealed a very different state of affairs. Complaints about extreme difficulty in filling science vacancies were widespread, and often retired science teachers have returned part time so that classes could continue. Obviously our schools are being starved of science teachers.

Why is this so? Why has teaching become unpopular? Before the war there was no shortage of science teachers; there were always several applications from suitably qualified people for any vacant post. Now, even when all sorts of extra inducements such as housing and extra allowances are offered, an advertisement may produce either no replies, or else one or two completely unsuitable ones.

Many responsible bodies have published reports on the shortage, for it is one which alarms the public in general, and industry and educational authorities in particular. The National Advisory Council on the Training and Supply of Teachers has considered the problem and made recommendations; so have the Federation of British Industries, and the Science Masters Association. The subject has been discussed at the Home Universities Conference, and at conferences up and down the country.

Financial aspects of shortage

The financial position appears high on all lists. It is generally agreed that industry can and will outbid all its competitors in the manpower field. Teaching salary scales are low; they do not distinguish between science graduates for whom there is a great demand, and arts graduates who may find difficulty in obtaining a job in any other field; they make only a very slight distinction between graduates and non-graduates, despite the difference in training.

There have been increases in salary, but these have of necessity been very small. There were in 1954 approximately 264,319 teachers in service in Great Britain; of these, 16,734 were graduates in science and technology.[1] Only a certain amount of money is available for increases in salary for teachers; this may be given either to all the teachers or to the scientifically trained graduates only.

Obviously, for attracting more science graduates into the teaching profession, the latter would be more effective; however, it is considered by many people that this would put science teachers in an invidious position in the staff room. The champions of 'more money for science teachers' point out that in the universities, lecturers and professors in the Faculties of Medicine are paid more than their colleagues in other faculties, and that this has not produced any serious problems. Everybody realizes that this is the only way of obtaining people to teach Medicine. However, the members of the Science Masters Association themselves have rejected the idea of a differential as they consider that the whole profession is underpaid.

The teaching profession in general tends to take an unrealistic attitude towards this problem; when various expedients for relieving the shortage are suggested, practising teachers often express strong disapproval. They fear that the wrong type may become teachers; they want only those with a vocation to join

[1] *Annual Report of the Ministry of Education*, H.M.S.O., London, 1955.

them; they are reluctant to abolish compulsory teacher-training courses in case standards of entry to their profession become lowered.

Often a science master is paid more than his classics colleague, by the judicious use of special responsibility and advanced teaching allowances, but while such inducements may attract a teacher from another school, they will rarely be effective in drawing an undecided graduate into the fold.

Inadequate laboratory assistance in schools

The National Advisory Council for the Training and Supply of Teachers points out:

Through lack of laboratory assistants science teachers in many schools are having to spend much time cleaning and servicing apparatus, preparing stock solutions, washing bottles and generally keeping their laboratories in safe and efficient working order.

The Council considers that this will probably lower the actual quality of the science teaching given, since teachers without adequate assistance will tend to cut down on practical work and become black-board teachers. All interested bodies have recommended that laboratory assistants should be employed in all schools; the lack of them, while it is not sufficiently important to keep graduates out of teaching, helps to make it an unattractive career.

Lack of career prospects in teaching

It has been suggested that a major feature of science teaching is the lack of career prospects. The teacher receives a small annual increment, and unless he receives promotion to the headship of a department or school (promotions which by their nature come only to the few), he can estimate to the last farthing his income until his retirement, and the prospect is not enticing. To combat this, the Federation of British Industries has suggested a promotion ladder with four grades, each with its own salary scale, and so linked that a teacher would receive an immediate increase on being promoted from one scale to the next, and would then receive the annual increments of his new scale up to the agreed maximum. This would offer a career with good prospects, and would help to attract the better graduates.

Quality of new science teachers

There have been many complaints that those scientists who are now becoming teachers are in general of poorer quality, or at least have poorer degrees than those who entered before the war. A recent report[1] classified science teachers in sixty-six grammar schools in the north-west of England both by class of degree and by age. On the assumption that most teachers enter the profession soon after graduation, this provides a measure of the varying quality of entrants over a period of time.

NUMBER OF SCIENCE GRADUATES (MEN/WOMEN) ACCORDING TO THE CLASS OR TYPE OF DEGREE & YEAR OF BIRTH

Class of Degree	Years of Birth														
	Before 1900			1900–1909			1910–1919			1920 and later			TOTAL		
	M.	F.	%	M.	F.	%	M.	F.	%	M.	F.	%	M.	F.	%
1st class Hon.	5	1	7	20	1	14	9	1	7	7	1	5	41	4	8
2nd class Hon.	28	2	36	57	4	42	71	4	50	46	8	34	202	18	42
3rd (4th) class Hon.	6	1	9	24	0	16	22	1	15	21	2	14	73	4	15
Pass	36	3	48	31	8	28	40	3	28	61	14	47	168	28	35
TOTALS	75	7	100	132	13	100	142	9	100	135	25	100	484	54	100

It will be noted that those teachers born since 1920 are of lower academic standard than their predecessors who entered the profession in the nineteen-thirties.

This has happened only in scientific subjects. A comparison[2] of the academic standards of Arts teachers with those of Science teachers gives the following results.

[1] *The Staffing of Grammar Schools.* Egner and Young. Liverpool University Press, Liverpool, 1954.
[2] Egner and Young, op. cit.

NUMBER OF SCIENCE & ARTS GRADUATES WITH FIRST- & SECOND-CLASS HONOURS DEGREES, ACCORDING TO THEIR YEAR OF BIRTH

Degree	Before 1900			1900–1909			1910–1919			1920 & later			TOTAL		
	M.	*F.*	*%*	*M.*	*F.*	*%*	*M.*	*F.*	*%*	*M.*	*F.*	*%*	*M.*	*F.*	*%*
Science & Maths	33	3	43	77	5	56	80	5	57	53	9	39	243	22	50
Arts	43	7	43	108	16	66	175	20	76	200	44	74	526	87	69

On the assumption that the child is influenced by his teachers (and one does hope that the assumption is true) then the sciences are at a disadvantage; they are not being expounded by first-class men, while the humanities are. This could have a serious effect on the numbers taking science subjects.

Chances of headmastership

It has also been suggested that Science masters do not stand as good a chance of promotion to headmasterships as do their Arts colleagues. Egner and Young investigated the academic background of headmasters and headmistresses in their sample, with the following results.[1]

PROPORTION OF SPECIALISTS TEACHERS WHO HAVE BECOME HEADMASTERS

Arts Degrees		Science Degrees	
Subject	*Proportion*	*Subject*	*Proportion*
Divinity	1 in 12·7	Mathematics	1 in 16·2
English	1 in 23·0	Biology	1 in 26·4
History	1 in 8·5	Chemistry	1 in 25·4
Geography	1 in 70·0	Physics	1 in 26·1
Mod. Lang.	1 in 18·3	All Science	1 in 19·9
Classics	1 in 10·2		
All Arts	1 in 15·4		

(The proportion in all subjects was 1 in 19·1)

It will be noticed that apart from mathematicians, scientists stand a below average chance of a headmastership. It has been argued that since few scientists with first-class degrees are entering teaching now, the proportion of science headmasters

[1] Egner and Young, op. cit.

will inevitably be low. This will almost certainly apply in the future, but the headmasters of today will in general have entered the teaching profession twenty or more years ago, when first-class scientists did take up teaching, and in consequence scientists should be well represented among the headmasters. The fact that they are not so represented must be a definite deterrent to many possible teachers.

Widespread aversion to teaching

But perhaps the most important thing is that teaching is widely considered by the graduates of today as a dull occupation, and as a last resort if nothing better can be found. In contrast, industry, the Scientific Civil Service, and the various research establishments seem to offer a more interesting life, where 'something is always happening'. This counter-attraction has sometimes been described as 'the appeal of research'. I think that it is rather a desire to be actively engaged in making something rather than to drift into the monastic backwater which many young people consider teaching to be. The young graduate of today is afraid that his normal mature development would be stunted by constant contact with children, and that in consequence it would be preferable to work among adults. This is unfortunate, as we need able people to teach our children.

Possible remedies

Nevertheless one knows many graduates who would readily take up teaching, or indeed any other job, if the salary scales were sufficiently attractive. The need for science teachers is great; some action on salaries is clearly necessary.

It is also to be hoped that more scientifically-trained women will enter the teaching profession. There is a grave shortage of women science teachers, particularly in girls' schools. Teaching is a career to which women are particularly suited. They will probably be conscientious; the feeling of security and the lack of adventure which often discourage the able male scientist may attract the female; for her, too, the respectability of this career will be a point in its favour. The strongest recommendation of all is that a teaching post may be easily combined with marriage because of the short hours and long vacations.

As a temporary measure, there are a number of ways in which the shortage may be alleviated. Married women are obvious recruits for full-time or part-time science teaching; however, most schools now readily employ them, and the possible increase here is not great. The retirement age for school teachers could be raised as many of them retire before they wish to do so. Leave of absence for research might be another inducement. Increased facilities for general science degrees might help; many people unable to complete an honours degree would be able to take a general science degree and then teach. Arts graduates could be taught additional mathematics in their teacher-training year.

The schools themselves can help: arrangements by two or three schools in the same area to have joint science classes would give a great saving. This does happen in some areas, but on a very small scale.

Many people in other professions might be prepared to consider changing to science teaching, if their new salary made due allowance for their previous experience (as happens to a limited extent in technical colleges). One cannot expect a rush of applicants here; industry will always be able to outbid the schools, but a few people may be gained. The cuts in the Armed Forces offer a possible new source of supply to this field, but very few scientifically qualified people will be released, as they will be an essential part of the reorganized Forces. It may, however, be possible to re-train some of those who are redundant and who have an adequate educational background to become teachers of junior science.

Laboratory technicians

In the discussion on the shortage of science teachers, the need for adequate laboratory assistance in schools was raised. Often local authorities, governing bodies, or headmasters do not recognize the necessity for such assistance; in others while they may acknowledge its desirability, they just cannot afford to pay a technician. But even where the need has been recognized, and the money is available, there is often difficulty in obtaining suitable assistance. Laboratory technicians themselves are in short supply in the schools.

There are many reasons for this; perhaps the main one is that such jobs are often underpaid and are widely regarded as 'dead end'. The technician is often expected to know the fundamentals of several subjects, and to be skilled in certain techniques, and yet he rarely has the opportunity of becoming more than a technician.

To help remove this dead-end aspect, the Science Masters Association has advised that a scheme of training and promotion for technicians should be established. They recommended the establishment of four grades of technician in schools:

Grade I.   Assistant Laboratory Technician (up to 21st birthday but unqualified).

Grade II.   Laboratory Technician, Lower Grade. Over 21 but unqualified (unless covered by Grade III).

Grade III. Laboratory Technician, Higher Grade. Over 21 with
        (a) suitable qualifications by examination,
    or (b) long experience and recommendation by science teacher and headmaster,
    or (c) suitable industrial laboratory assistance,

Grade IV.   By promotion from Grade III.

The qualification recommended is the Laboratory Technicians Certificate of the City and Guilds of London Institute, and good salary scales are envisaged for the higher grades. This is an obvious occupation for girls who have reached a reasonable level in Physics and Chemistry (G.C.E. 'O' level) but who do not wish to continue to 'A' level or further. What is needed to attract these young women into the laboratory is a better salary at the lower levels; at present a young assistant is rarely paid more than £300 per annum, while the same girl in a secretarial job would receive more.

It is not only in schools that laboratory technicians are needed; industry also wants them. But industry recognizes its need; firms do not want a scientist to waste his time making up his own solutions when someone less highly trained (and less highly paid) can do the job just as efficiently; in consequence adequate assistance is generally provided, and adequate salaries are paid.

Draughtsmen

During the course of its case studies, the Science and Industry Committee was naturally told repeatedly of the seriousness of the shortage of draughtsmen. There are a number of contributory factors to this shortage; the tremendous expansion of industry and the greater number of calls made on the design section have increased the demand for draughtsmen and one suspects that many employers have been taken by surprise.

In the aircraft industry, for example, separate teams of draughtsmen in one firm often work on alternative designs for the same aircraft; at the same time most of the other aircraft firms are trying to capture the same contract, so that armies of draughtsmen are needed in this one branch of industry alone. So many new developments have called for the services of the draughtsman; automation has meant some elaborate designing; new synthetic materials required new machinery for their production; the Atomic Energy Authority called for large numbers of draughtsmen because of their new buildings and equipment; and the large number of new models produced by the automobile industry in its effort to capture and retain export markets called for further armies of designers.

The demand has increased; what of the supply?

The traditional method of training for a draughtsman has always been either a trade or an engineering apprenticeship, coupled with evening classes. The engineering apprentice will probably spend some time in the drawing office, and if he shows the necessary aptitude he may become a draughtsman at the conclusion of his apprenticeship. He will be expected to attend further classes and obtain probably the Ordinary and Higher National Certificates.

The craft apprentice may be upgraded to the drawing office either during his apprenticeship or after its completion. He will also be expected to obtain the National Certificates. His basic remuneration as a draughtsman will be higher than the basic rate which he would have received had he remained in the workshops; but since the skilled tradesman may be paid more than the minimum rate, may earn a bonus, may have piecework earnings and may do a large amount of overtime at enhanced rates of pay, the draughtsman may be the poorer of the two.

Before the Second World War, draughtsmen had a great deal of prestige in the world of industry: they had better holidays and working conditions and received benefits such as sickness payments which were not available to the manual worker. Now conditions for both groups are similar, and since the draughtsman is not necessarily as well paid as the manual worker, there is very little incentive for a boy to enter the drawing office from the works. In addition, production engineering has now become a recognized career, and it is much easier to reach the top by this path than through the drawing office.

The engineering apprentice now tends to be a boy with a public- or grammar-school education and with some subjects at G.C.E. 'O' Level; he will spend his apprenticeship in different parts of the works and in the different laboratories or research offices. Towards the end of this time some decision as to his future career will be made, and he will now usually set his sights much higher than the drawing board. The influx of trained engineers and scientists into industry has tended to depress the status of the draughtsman.

Thus the drawing office is being starved of new entrants from both of its former sources. Many firms have tried to institute special training schemes to meet the shortage, and have given youths a brief course in draughtsmanship. This is opposed by established draughtsmen who consider that practical experience is essential since a draughtsman does not merely draw; he has to use his judgement and often he designs parts of a structure. It is worth remembering however that in France draughts-manship is taught as a trade in the apprenticeship centres to boys who have received only primary education.

Borderline technologists

A further shortage is in the 'borderline' technologies where men who have been well trained in two separate disciplines are needed; chemical engineering is one obvious example. In this country there are very few courses in chemical engineering as such, and a man who has been trained in either chemistry or engineering has no difficulty in obtaining a job immediately. Few people will, therefore, undertake the necessary additional training required by the chemical engineer. In Continental countries adequate courses in chemical engineering are more common; and the training is both deep and thorough. This is one field where we can learn from the example of others.

CHAPTER IX

TECHNOLOGICAL TRAINING
IN OTHER COUNTRIES

France

In France, as in England, primary education lasts until the age of eleven; some children remain in the primary school and take either the ordinary course terminating at fourteen, or a higher general or technical course (cours complémentaire). The latter lasts for four years, and leads to a certificate which admits the pupil after a competitive examination either to a teacher-training college or to the second cycle of the course in the lycée (grammar school).

In general, the more able children will leave the primary school for the lycée or collège at eleven. Here the course is divided into two cycles, one of four years, the other of three. During the first cycle there are various streams whose courses are basically the same, and in all some science is taken by the children.

During the second cycle there is some measure of specialization (see diagram) but no irrevocable step is taken. In theory one may take the first part of the Baccalauréat (at 16–17) in any of the given groups, and then take any of the possible subjects in the second (or specialized) part one year later. In practice children tend to continue with the same subjects; they would find some difficulty in changing, as their grounding in the new subjects would be insufficient.

The classical tradition in French education is still very strong, but the official policy is now one of encouragement for the sciences, because of the grave shortage of scientists and science teachers. Suitable provision is made for all the grades of technologist and technician required.

Those who are to become engineering technicians leave the primary school for a Collège Technique or one of the Ecoles Nationales Professionelles, to which entrance is by examination. Here education to approximately sixth-form standard is given, with the emphasis on engineering and technical subjects. In these schools it is possible to take the Baccalauréat in Technical Sciences, and thence to proceed to the great engineering schools. In this way no limits are set to the heights which may be reached. Naturally, most of the pupils will not continue to this level, but the opportunity is there.

The higher educational system may be divided into two main sections; universities and engineering schools (Les Grandes Ecoles). The Baccalauréat gives automatic entrance to the former but for the latter the holders of the Baccalauréat have to sit a competitive examination.

Higher education is regarded as being divided into three cycles.

(A) *Propedéutique*

The first year of the university is a preparatory year (Année Propedéutique). On the science side it is divided into three sections: General Mathematics; Mathematics, Physics, and Chemistry; and Physics, Chemistry, and Natural Sciences. Approximately half of the students take two years to achieve a sufficiently good examination mark to be allowed to continue with the rest of the course.

There are post-Baccalauréat classes in the lycée for those who want to enter the engineering schools. In theory two years' preparation is needed, but in practice this period often extends to three. The main subject during this time is mathematics (about seventeen hours a week); courses in Physics and Chemistry are also given. Theoretically each of the seventeen schools has its own entrance examination programme, but in practice the schools (which are all controlled by the Ministry of Education) are divided into three or four groups for the purpose of this examination.

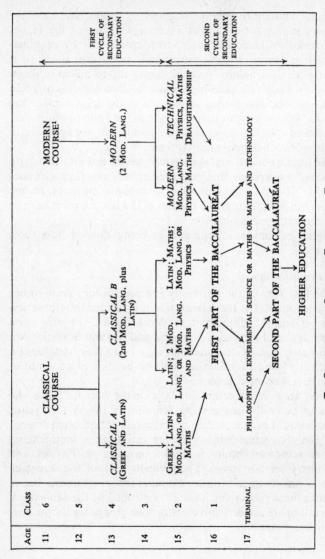

THE ORGANIZATION OF SECONDARY EDUCATION IN FRANCE

[1] There is also a special Modern Course for those who leave school at fourteen.

(B) *Obtaining the Licence or Diploma*

The university system is one of certificates; the Licence is granted to a student with three certificates, and a completed Année Propedéutique. These certificates may be general or special depending on the degree of specialization in the course. The teaching for each certificate is completely independent of any other. They may be taken in any order, and provided that the time tables do not clash, a student may take two certificates in one year. All Licences are not equal; only some give the right to sit the teachers' examination. To teach science, one must have certificates in Physics (general), Chemistry (general), and Mathematics. In Experimental Science there are public lectures at which attendance is not compulsory, but all practical courses must be attended. Tests are held at frequent intervals, and a student who fails two or three of these is not permitted to sit the examination for the certificate.

In the engineering schools, a two-year course in general science and engineering followed by a one-year course in the speciality of the particular school leads to the diploma of the school. Many of the students follow the university courses and obtain certificates and because of the extent of their study of fundamental science and mathematics they can obtain a Licence with two certificates and their diploma; no Année Propedéutique is necessary.

The engineering schools have very great prestige, and their diplomas are often more highly prized than a Licence.

(C) *Research training, or preparation for teaching examinations*

The method of training for this third stage varies. It is possible to carry out research directly for one of the doctorate degrees:

    (i) *Doctorat d'Etat.* For this a teaching Licence is a necessary preliminary. This doctorate is an essential, but not a sufficient, qualification for a university chair. The period of research is three to four years.

    (ii) *Ingénieur Docteur.* A Licence is not required as a

necessary preliminary, because this degree is designed for students from the engineering schools. The period of research is three to four years.

(iii) *Doctorat de Specialité*.   To obtain this degree one-year post-graduate courses in a particular field and one year's research in this field are necessary. At the end of the two years a thesis is presented. The students may be divided into groups of between twenty and thirty and so it is possible for them to be given much more individual attention than an undergraduate receives.

To become a teacher the candidate must have obtained a Licence and the Certificat d'Aptitudes Pédagogiques de l'Enseignement Secondaires (CAPES) before he is allowed to enter the Concours (competition) for teachers. This examination tests teacher training, and is also an examination of specialization. The candidate tries to become a teacher of Physics, or Mathematics, etc.

A year after obtaining the CAPES, the student enters the Concours, which because of the centralized system of French education, is for all France. There is a very difficult written examination which lasts for three or four days. Those who pass this stage then have an oral examination to test their teaching qualities.

Successful candidates then teach in a lycée under the direction of a teacher; this is the Stage Pédagogique, during which he is visited by an Inspector. Finally he sits another examination on teaching practice, and if successful becomes a recognized teacher.

There is a second and more difficult Concours (Agrégation); for this it is necessary to have either CAPES, or a Licence and one year's research. The preparation for this competition is carried out in the university.

A series of written papers each lasting six or seven hours, eliminates a number of the candidates. The remainder then undergo two 'trials by jury'; they are given between three and four hours to prepare a subject, on which they have to talk for three-quarters of an hour before a panel of examiners. In addition, apparatus for two lessons must be prepared, although the lessons themselves need not be given.

Each year between twenty and twenty-five scientists, most of them teachers, pass Agrégation. Only two or three remain in the teaching profession; the majority prepare a doctorate thesis (usually Doctorat d'Etat) and try to obtain university posts. This has made the shortage of science teachers even more acute.

It may be seen that educational standards are high, and that the whole educational process is highly selective. In fact, many people in France feel that possibly the standards, particularly for entrance to the engineering schools, are set so high that a number of the unsuccessful candidates would be quite capable of becoming good engineers. It must be remembered that these students will normally have attained a high standard in the Baccalauréat, and will have carried out post-Baccalauréat studies of a high level for two or three years.

To remedy what seems to be an injustice, it has been recommended that a new engineering school should be set up in Lyons. For this school there would be no Concours, but instead the first year would be probationary; students who were considered unsuitable for the Diploma would then be directed towards higher technical courses.

The title 'engineer' is protected in France; it can be used to describe only a graduate of one of the Grandes Ecoles, in which very high standards are maintained. These graduates have been taught the elements of law and economics in addition to having received a thorough grounding in science and in engineering. Some on-the-job training for the new graduates is necessary, but after that the engineer rises quickly to the top because of the breadth of his training.

There are many women students in the scientific sections of the Universities, particularly in Biology and Chemistry, and some of the Professors of Mathematics in Paris are women.

However, very few women enter the Engineering Schools. They are barred from the Polytechnique, the School of Mining, and the School of Bridges and Roads, and while they may enter the others if they wish, it is not customary. There are very few opportunities for women engineers in industry.

In the past it was necessary to have men teachers in boys' schools and women teachers in girls' schools. In view of the grave shortage of men science teachers, women are now permitted to teach in boys' schools; as yet very few are doing this.

Similarly, the training at the lower levels is not left to chance. While traditional apprenticeship still exists in France, it is being superseded by training in the apprenticeship centres, which students enter at fourteen.

In contrast to the more academic side of the educational system which is highly centralized, the apprenticeship centres have very strong local affiliations. Their governing committees are composed of equal numbers of Trade Union representatives and nominees of the Ministry of Education. Trades appropriate to the industries of the district are taught.

The centres are not simply trade schools; half of the time is devoted to general education, which is integrated with the remainder of the course as far as is possible. In addition to what are normally considered trades in Britain, such courses as tourism and draughtsmanship are included.

For the first six months the pupil studies three trades. During this period he is carefully observed and is then advised as to his most suitable main course. If he wishes he may select an alternative trade, but he must maintain a definite standard if he is to be allowed to stay at the centre.

After three years there is a series of examinations on the results of which are awarded Certificates of Practical Aptitude in the chosen craft. Most students pass these tests with ease, since the centres demand a very high standard of workmanship during the course.

All costs are covered by the State. Where necessary, boarding centres have been established and in addition needy pupils have been given small weekly grants, in lieu of wages, to take home.

Students have the normal school holiday of two months in the summer.

In France, career decisions are not left to chance; an extremely thorough system of vocational guidance has been in existence for some time.

In 1922, the Technical Section of the Ministry of Education was authorized to investigate the physical, intellectual and personal qualities required in different kinds of work. At about the same time the Paris Chamber of Commerce began to carry out experiments in vocational guidance for schoolchildren. In 1938 it became compulsory for every département to set up vocational guidance centres. The counsellors, who are mainly university graduates or primary-school teachers, are carefully selected by examination, interview, and practical tests, and must take a two-years' training course. There is a legal obligation upon the school and parents to present the school leaver (if he or she is leaving at the minimum age) for examination at one of the centres and to supply the information needed by the counsellors. The guidance starts at the beginning of the child's last year at school with a special conference between the teachers and counsellors.

Group intelligence, technical ability and performance tests are first of all given to the class by the teacher, and work is started on the detailed reports which the school prepares for each pupil. The children are given questionnaires, in which they are asked to state their ambitions, views, and tastes. The counsellor then sees the children individually to give them further intelligence tests and tests of physical reactions and manipulative ability. A medical examination follows, given by a doctor who has taken a special course to prepare him for this work.

By this time there are nine or ten reports on each child, and the counsellor studies them prior to inviting the parents to discuss their child with him. The guidance centres maintain a remarkable store of information on jobs of all kinds, much of it gathered by counsellors during training. The parents are told of the child's potentialities, and suitable occupations are suggested, together with details of conditions and prospects.

The guidance service is also extended to pupils in the lycées and universities. A very comprehensive reference library keeps details of all careers, and in addition, details of higher education establishments are filed for the benefit of schoolchildren. Career programmes are given twice weekly on the national broadcasting system, and some are also given from local radio stations.

The service produces many publications, the main one giving all the new information which has been received. Copies of this are sent to all the regional educational centres, and so students in Bordeaux know as much about the possibilities in Lille or Strasbourg as do the students who live in those places.

These regional centres then transmit information to the schools, in each of which is a teacher who devotes a specific number of hours to this work (for which he is paid extra). The centre will send any additional information which may be required.

This service is both very active and very comprehensive:

From the Ecole Polytechnique to the smallest Centre of Apprenticeship, surveys are established concerning all establishments belonging to the various educational systems. These documents specify particularly the values of the studies, their curriculum, their duration, the conditions of admission, the dates and nature of the examinations, entrance and final competitions, the system of entering, of scholarships and loans on trust, the possibilities offered to the pupils, etc. . . .[1]

Similarly detailed studies are produced for the various professions and occupations, on the state of the labour market, on guidance methods, and on particular vacancies.

The aim is to ensure that all children make the best use of the educational opportunities open to them, and that they enter careers to which they are suited. Most of the schools which offer vocational training at the lower levels have been started or developed since the war; such extensive action by the State indicates an awareness of the problem rarely found elsewhere.

[1] Note on the Activities of the University Board of Statistics and Educational and Vocational Documentation in France.

The Federal Republic of Germany

Since the end of the war, Germany has expanded its resources for training scientists and technologists at a fantastic rate. This is particularly noticeable in North-Rhine-Westphalia, the wealthiest of the States (and the one which contains the Ruhr).

Nowhere is this more apparent than at the Technische Hochschule (Technological University) at Aachen. The Technische Hochschule, which now has a student population of 6500 and a teaching staff of 650, has been built up from practically nothing during the past eleven years. There was a very small university here before the war, but 70 per cent of it was blitzed, and so almost all of the buildings are new. The cost of over 40,000,000 D.M. has been met by the North-Rhine-Westphalia Government.

The University is effectively a town, with a great variety of large buildings spread over a wide area. Everything has been beautifully designed and finished, and room has been left for expansion. A number of new institutes are planned. There is a student village with accommodation for 170 students; this is effectively a club whose student council considers applications for vacancies.

The minimum time for completion of the Dipl. Ing. course is four years, but the average student takes five. The first two years are devoted to general training, and the remainder to specialized courses. One year's practical work is obligatory, and the students normally do six months before entering the university and the remainder during vacations. (The former is possible since the Abitur[1] examination is in March and the Winter Semester starts in November.) A Diploma-project must also be completed; this takes nine to twelve months in Chemistry and Physics, and about three months in Engineering.

This Diploma-project is characteristic of German technological training, and is included in the course because it is felt that a student should show his ability to carry through a complete design or research project himself, with a very limited

[1] Abitur corresponds to G.C.E. 'A' level examinations.

amount of guidance. Because of this, the Dipl. Ing. is usually equated to a British M.Sc. degree.

A teaching staff of about 650 includes 65 professors. Salaries seem higher than in Britain; an assistant receives £900, a kustos (who is of lower status than a lecturer) earns upwards of £1200.

There are over 600 foreign students, many of them from India. The student population is predominantly male; the few women students are mostly in the pharmacy and architecture institutes. All the institutes are up to date. In the machine-tool research centre, where research groups work on problems within the general framework of the research programme, there are a number of automatic transfer machines (often presents from industry). Electrical discharge equipment for manufacturing work pieces is being perfected, and one group has developed a method of photographing the manufacture of certain tools by synchronizing a stroboscope with the revolutions of the cutting-wheel. A number of mechanics are employed here, some apprentices are trained, and courses are given to students, but these are all regarded as subsidiary to the main research programme.

The Physics Institute is carrying out research on nuclear reactions at high temperatures, and in addition methods of photographing the lung to show up cancer are being investigated. Here again the equipment is most impressive.

The main block of lecture halls is one of the sights of post-war Germany, as every conceivable gadget has been incorporated. The actual shapes of the halls, staircases, and seats have been determined from an acoustical point of view; lighting may be varied to give any desired effect; and the lecturer need not turn his back to write on a board: he simply writes on a pad in front of him, and this is projected on to a screen. A series of projectors and screens have been fitted up, so that slides may be compared; and film projectors are also available. There has been no attempt to cut expenses here; everything needed has been supplied.

The prestige of Aachen and of the Technischen Hochschulen

generally is very high. These universities date only from about 1919, but they soon became pre-eminent because of the quality of work carried out, and the high standards demanded. The title Dipl. Ing. which is awarded is held in high esteem; even more so is the higher degree Dr. Ing.

The normal preparation for entry to one of the Technischen Hochschulen is given in the Gymnasium or Oberschule (grammar school) which children enter at the age of ten. It is possible to obtain entry to a Hochschule via the other schools but this rarely happens.

Very highly trained technicians are produced by the Ingenieurschule (or technical college), which gives full-time courses of three years to students who have generally attended the Mittelschule (or technical school) and have had some practical experience. Graduates of these colleges are entitled to call themselves engineers while graduates of the technological universities are diplômed-engineers. Both titles are protected.

As in France, apprenticeship training is taken very seriously. The school-leaver of fourteen may become an apprentice; after three and a half years during which time he must by law spend one day per week on vocational education either in the works or in the local Berufsschule (trade school), he will be ready to take the practical examination for his Journeyman's Certificate. There is no age limit to apprenticeship and one sometimes finds older men learning a trade.

The apprentice is not employed on production except where this is an absolutely essential part of his training. He may take a full-time course at a Berufsschule for either the whole period of normal apprenticeship, or a shorter period. If he takes the whole course he may enter industry as a fully-fledged craftsman; a shorter course will lead to some remission of the apprenticeship period.

The Berufsschulen are usually well supported by local firms which provide equipment and money; in addition, they receive generous grants from the State and can usually buy all that they need.

The more able pupils may sit a special examination (at

Years				
7	VOLKSSCHULE (Primary School)	VOLKSSCHULE	VOLKSSCHULE	VOLKSSCHULE (Primary School)
8				
9				
10	OBERSCHULE, GYMNASIUM (Grammar School)	MITTELSCHULE (Secondary, Technical, or Modern School)	BERUFSSCHULE (Trade School)	APPRENTICESHIP
11				
12				
13				
14				
15		MIDDLE EXAMINATION		CRAFTSMAN
16		PRACTICAL TRAINING		
17				
18		SPECIAL CERTIFICATE TO ENTER TECHNICAL COLLEGE		
19	ABITUR	INGENIEURSCHULE (Technical College)		
20	TECHNISCHE HOCHSCHULE (Technological University)		ENGINEER	
21				
22				
23	DIPL. ING.			
24	RESEARCH (in some cases)			
25	DR. ING.			
26	ENGINEER DIPLÔMED			

THE PATHS TO AN ENGINEERING CAREER IN GERMANY

seventeen) for entrance to the Ingenieurschule; it is thus possible for them to become engineers.

Vocational guidance is given to all who leave school at fourteen. Children are helped to select a trade or occupation, and their progress is followed. The first three months of an apprenticeship is regarded as the probationary period, and it is possible for a transfer to another trade to be made during this time.

It is very rare for a craftsman to reach a higher position in industry; one of the characteristics of the German system seems to be the definite caste structure imposed by the educational background.

Italy

Those who are concerned about early specialization in our schools would do well to consider the educational system in Italy, where it is not necessary to specialize in scientific subjects at school in order to study science or engineering at the university.

When the schoolchildren leave the primary school at eleven they have a choice between two types of school, the Scuola Media (middle school or junior grammar school) and the vocational training school. The middle school course lasts for three years; that is, until the pupils are fourteen. At this point a further division takes place; children may continue their general education in either Classical or Scientific Schools, or may start vocational training in Institutes of Art, Teacher-Training Schools, Commercial Institutes, or Technical Institutes.

Both the Classical and the Scientific Schools insist on a very high standard of general education. Some science is taught in the Classical Schools, besides Latin, Greek, and general arts subjects including languages; in the Scientific Schools a modern language is taught instead of Greek. Both types of school maintain very high standards in Mathematics.

Only pupils from the Classical Schools are eligible for professions such as the Law and the Church; in fact, most students in all faculties including Science and Engineering come from the Classical Schools, whose prestige is much higher than that of the Scientific Schools. This system tends to be self-perpetuating, as the better teachers are attracted to the Classical rather than to the Scientific Schools. Consequently the universities prefer their students to have come from the Classical Schools, while parents are relieved that no problems of early specialization arise.

The Scientific schools do, however, provide some students for the universities, but most of their pupils become clerical and semi-professional workers.

Engineering students are trained either within the general universities or at the big Technological Institutions of Milan and Turin. Technicians are provided by the Technical Institutes.

The general pattern of higher technological education is that the first two years are spent studying a general course of Mathematics, Mechanics, Physics, Mineralogy, and two foreign languages. These subjects provide a good foundation for the following three years, which are spent in one of the departments or Institutes of the Engineering Faculty, during which time specialized courses of a high standard are given. At the conclusion of the five-year course the examinations for the primary degree (the doctorate) are taken.

It is worthy of note that in Bologna, said to be the oldest university in the world, there is a flourishing Engineering Faculty; among the equipment in regular use are digital and analogue computers, and some apparatus for producing very high voltages. In the Aeronautics Institute some wind tunnels are almost ready for use. Similarly, the Engineering Faculty in Rome is well equipped and maintains academic standards that are very high. Engineering does not seem to be in any sense a 'poor relation' in a country where one would expect the classics to be all-important.

The academic staff are actively engaged in helping industries and public bodies, and much sponsored research is carried out. For example, problems of irrigation and power are studied in the universities, and dams and other structures are designed.

Engineering graduates rise quickly to the top of their profession because of their thorough training, and they continue to maintain very close contact with the universities. Therefore industrial firms are able to derive great benefit from university research.

The completely general education given in the Classical Schools does prevent a wastage of potential engineers through a wrong choice of subject; on the other hand, there is a certain rigidity in the social and educational systems which must mean some loss of able people. Nevertheless, Italy is producing large numbers of exceptionally well-trained engineers and technologists and we can learn a great deal from her example.

Switzerland

Switzerland, although a very small country, possesses nine institutions of university standing. The principal centres for technological training are the Eidgenössiche Technische Hochschule (the Swiss Federal Institute of Technology, known as the E.T.H.) in Zurich, and the Ecole Polytechnique of the University of Lausanne. As these two institutions follow the same programme, it is possible for a student to transfer from one to the other without difficulty.

The entrance qualification demanded by the universities is the Certificat de Maturité (the Swiss Baccalauréat). In general, foreign students are insufficiently prepared in mathematics (particularly in descriptive geometry) for admission to the first year of the course. Thus British candidates with three 'A' and three 'O' level subjects in G.C.E. must attend a preliminary course in Special Mathematics, and may then embark on the Diploma course in the following year. Students with an American B.Sc. will in general be admitted to the first year of the course without examination, although in some cases they are excused only part of the entrance examination.

The Diploma course lasts for nine terms (four and a half years); during the first four terms the basic sciences are studied, and professional studies occupy the remaining five. During the final term a Diploma-project must be completed. A growing number of students work for doctorates, which may usually be obtained in under two years.

There are in the E.T.H. eleven schools for professional training. In one of these the student will spend his final five terms. There is in addition a general section with many courses in history, philology, philosophy, politics, and economics. All students must take at least one course in the general section during each of his nine terms.

It is possible to specialize in industrial engineering: courses in production engineering and management training are given along with the normal engineering courses, and the Diploma-project is then the solution of a specific problem in an industrial organization. These graduates will then be mechanical or electrical engineers with management qualifications (and not just managers).

The schools of the E.T.H. are exceptionally large and well equipped. A notable feature is the rational design of the buildings, for example, in the siting of various common services. There has been a great deal of new building, and it is obvious that money is plentiful.

The universities and industry work together very closely. Many members of the staff of the E.T.H. have come from industry, and a number of the Chairs are held on a part-time basis by directors of industrial research departments. In addition, many industrial research projects are carried out in the university.

Designers, works directors, and assistants, are trained in Technical Institutes which are similar to the Ingenieurschulen in Germany. These schools are not of university status, but many of their former students hold leading positions in industry. Entrants must have had at least two or three years' practical experience; in fact, most of them have completed an apprenticeship. Further theoretical and practical work is given in a full-time course of approximately three years, and the graduate is then capable of taking a responsible industrial position.

Some of the Institutes run courses of a lower standard, and in particular a number contain apprenticeship schools where a thorough training in the chosen craft is given. Students taking these courses may then proceed to higher courses immediately or may interpose a short period in industry.

The engineering graduates receive an excellent training, not only in their own subjects but also in the humanities, due to the excellent education given in schools and the general courses in the university. It is not surprising, therefore, that engineers are very well paid, and that they occupy leading positions in Swiss industry.

Union of Soviet Socialist Republics

The Soviet Union produces annually large numbers of engineers and scientists. One of the reasons for this is the bias in favour of practical training; this tendency is increased by recent changes planned for the educational system.

Children under seven attend crêches and nursery schools which have been set up for the children of working women (almost all Russian women). At seven the primary school takes over, this stage lasting four years. The next three years constitute the intermediate stage, which may be either general or may be spent in a trade school. Education for these seven years is compulsory, although this has not been fully implemented in some outlying areas.

Those who continue their education beyond this point may spend three years in the upper grades (8, 9, 10) or may attend secondary semi-professional schools which offer a two- to four-year training in such subjects as nursing, dentistry, veterinary surgery, technical draughtsmanship, teaching, and machine building. Those who pass the leaving examination set at the end of the tenth-grade year are awarded a 'maturity certificate'. Graduation from a secondary semi-professional school is regarded as equivalent to gaining a maturity certificate for the purposes of higher education. There are also military schools which correspond to ten-year schools and are for sons of members of the Soviet Officers Corps.

The control of all education is centralized, and there is uniformity over the whole country. Even class examinations are set by the State on a nation-wide basis.

In some parts of the country, the ten grades are contained in one school. In others there is a seven-year school carrying education to the intermediate stage whilst in remote country districts there is often only a primary school and the children have to be transferred to another school at the close of the primary stage.

The whole educational process is highly selective and it has been estimated that for every thousand children who enter school, only forty-five are successful in obtaining the maturity certificate ten years later.[1]

Thirty-three universities and eight-hundred professional institutions cover the higher education field. Holders of a maturity certificate sit entrance examinations (for which short preparatory courses are given in the university) and must also be screened by a committee. Those students who obtain gold medals at school are excused the entrance examination.

A very high proportion of the available places (and scholarships) are in scientific subjects. During the five- to six-year course, science and engineering students attend between fifteen and twenty lectures per week and spend a great deal of time on practical work and study. Frequent tests are set, and since poor results lead to dismissal, the students work very hard. A degree project must be completed during the final six months. Many students stay for post-graduate research.

There are many women engineers and scientists. They readily embark on degree courses, and are readily employed when they graduate.

This is the situation at present, but a new law has just been introduced (December 1958), embodying radical changes in the educational system. The leaders of the country have expressed concern at the creation of an élite through the ten-year school. They have decided, however, not to proceed with ten-year schooling for all. Instead, all children will now attend school for eight years, and will complete their education on a part-time basis while undertaking useful work in the community.

[1] *Soviet Professional Manpower: Its Education, Training and Supply*, Nicholas De Witt, Russian Research Centre, Harvard University.

Many of the higher educational establishments will also work on a part-time basis.

Young people who combine study and work successfully will have their working day or week shortened considerably, and may be allowed to devote longer periods to study alone.

During the transition stage many of the ten-year schools will be retained to maintain an adequate supply of entrants to the higher educational establishments. It has been suggested that children who are exceptionally gifted in mathematics and science should be transferred to these schools.

Under the new system, some schools will accept entrants with an eight-year schooling and will give them a three-year course covering the remainder of the old school curriculum in addition to practical training. This seems to leave a loop-hole for the creation of a new élite.

Secondary semi-professional schools will now accept students who have been to the eight-year schools; the practical content of the curriculum will be increased.

It remains to be seen what effect these changes will have on the production of engineers and scientists. It seems unlikely that they will increase the flow, and a more likely result would be a decrease because to qualify would take at least one year longer. It is possible that gifted children may still be able to devote themselves to study; it is also possible that all these plans may be abandoned very hastily.

The United States of America

Most American children attend the local grade school (primary school) and the general high school. At the latter the pupils are awarded credits for the courses they attend satisfactorily and before they can graduate they must have gained a certain number of them. There is a wide range of subjects to choose from, and generally the pupils are allowed to decide for themselves what subjects they will study. Thus it is possible for both academic and non-academic types to select suitable courses.

After leaving high school at about seventeen, the American boy or girl may take an unskilled or skilled job, commence clerical work, or continue his education. There are two-year junior colleges offering general education, and four-year colleges and universities offering both general and professional education. Often the first degree is a general one, followed by training in medicine, law, engineering, etc. There is also a comprehensive scheme of post-graduate training with many specialized courses and opportunities for research work.

The basic idea behind American education is that of equal opportunity for everyone. This can lead to quite unsuitable people studying together, as 'streaming' is considered undemocratic. Academic standards at school and up to the first degree stage are at least two years lower than those prevailing in the United Kingdom; this is however counteracted by the high standards which are maintained in the graduate schools.

There is at present a great deal of concern in the United States about their technological training; teachers are not well paid and in consequence there is a shortage of mathematics and science teachers which seems even more acute than that in Britain, for in very many schools mathematical and scientific subjects have had to be cut out altogether.

Trained engineers are very highly regarded in America, and occupy the highest positions in industry. The rapidly expanding economy is creating a very great need for more trained people; it seems probable that this need will not be met.

Canada

There are two clearly defined types of education in Canada. The English tradition is followed in all the provinces except for Quebec. Here the French tradition is followed in the Roman Catholic schools while the Protestant schools are of the English tradition.

At the secondary level there are three types of school; the academic, the commercial, and the vocational. Students may attend any one of these provided they have completed primary school; there is no direction of pupils into one type or another, although non-directive counselling is given in the final primary-school year and in the early secondary-school years.

In the Roman Catholic schools of Quebec, the opportunities for girls are very limited. There is no co-education, and girls may follow primary school with a teacher-training or household-science school, or may attend a two-year course in a form of secondary school which leads to the schools of fine arts, commercial courses or nurse-training courses. Boys, on the other hand, may attend a classical college and obtain a Baccalauréat and then gain university entrance; they have also the option of entering scientific and technical schools which lead to the higher schools affiliated to the universities.

The majority of the engineers qualify by attending university; it is necessary to be a member of one of the Provincial Professional Engineering Associations before calling oneself a 'professional engineer', and many years of private study would be necessary for the non-graduate.

Technicians may be recruited from skilled tradesmen who have been given special advanced training; they may be graduates of special technical institutes at the junior college level; or they may be selected from those who have discontinued their university training. Draughtsmen are usually trained on the job, although in some places draughtsmanship is an apprenticed trade.

At present Canada is staffing many of her industrial firms with qualified engineers from Europe; this is helping to solve her own requirements, but is aggravating the shortage in European countries. Canadian graduates are in many cases being attracted across the border by the higher salaries paid in the United States.

CHAPTER X

SUMMARY AND CONCLUSIONS

In this chapter we shall summarize (on the basis of the information in earlier chapters) the main factors which affect the young people of this country during the years which determine their future careers, and which thus determine the supply of scientists and technologists.

Heredity

It may be said that one determining factor operates before the child is born, i.e. heredity. It seems reasonable to assume that there is some connection between the intelligence or ability of a child and that of his parents, although the nature and strength of this connection is obscure; when one adds to this the fact that in general the lower social groups have larger families than the higher (and presumably more intelligent) ones, it can be seen that there is the possibility that the proportion of more intelligent people in the community may fall. To some extent this trend is being reversed: for example it is now becoming more common for professional people to have large families, and a recent survey[1] showed that women graduates have more children than the rest of the population, and are much more fertile than others of similar background. This should help to keep the balance right; an adequate supply of intelligent people is a first essential for an adequate supply of highly-trained scientists, engineers and technologists.

Pre-school years

This is not all. When a child is born, he does not only acquire parents; he gains relatives, family friends, a share of a house, in fact a whole environment which will determine many aspects of his future existence. He may receive great care and attention, or

[1] *Wives who went to College.* Judith Hubback. Heinemann, London, 1957.

he may be neglected. His parents may be intelligent, well-educated and well-read, and anxious that he should be so too; his home may contain an ample supply of books which he is encouraged to read, or it may be bare of any intellectual fodder; the attitudes of his parents and companions may encourage the acquisition of skill and knowledge, or they may stunt and warp any efforts at self-improvement.

Thus while in theory when all children start school at five or six years old, they begin at the same point, in practice this is not so. There will already be obvious differences in their mental development, quite apart from levels of intelligence.

Primary education

But the factors which have produced these differences do not vanish when the child starts school; on the contrary, their effect will probably be intensified. One child will go home to work in a quiet room with no interruptions. He will be encouraged to discuss his work with his parents, and he will be wisely helped to discover answers to problems for himself. Other children will receive no such help, or only the assistance which discourages self-help, and many of them will not be able to overcome this handicap.

In these years also differences in educational background may begin to exercise their influence on later careers. In England a considerable proportion of children of the middle classes will go to private schools, which (though of varied quality) may have advantages of small classes and individual attention which the State schools lack. A small minority will go away at the age of eight or nine to a preparatory school, and will enter that privileged stream which expects to go *via* the Common Entrance Examination to a public school. The great majority of all children, however, will be engaged on courses which lead to the eleven-plus examination.

Selection at eleven-plus

The basis for this examination which is effectively for grammar-school selection, is in most areas performance in written

H   A.S.M.

tests in English and Arithmetic, and in an intelligence test from which the Intelligence Quotient (I.Q.) is measured. There does not seem to be as yet any way of measuring what one might call the 'intellectual stamina' of the candidates; that is that quality which will enable a boy or girl to continue working in the face of other distractions for a long period until a course of study has been satisfactorily completed. But since a high proportion of scientists and technologists require a grammar-school education, the effectiveness of the selection is a matter of much interest.

We have seen that by this time some children will already have acquired certain advantages over others, and it seems reasonable to assume that this will affect their chances in this examination. Furthermore, in some schools not all children have the opportunity of qualifying, for the school applies its own selection process before the main examination, and enters only those who are considered to have a good chance of 'passing'.

In addition, many parents may not want their child to have a grammar-school education, or may not actively assist him. This may be because they themselves are uneducated, and fear estrangement if their children develop interests foreign to the parents, and through their occupations enter a different social stratum. (Against this must be set the lofty ambitions which many parents have for their children.) The parents may also be alarmed by any requirement to give an undertaking to keep the child at school for a fixed period beyond the statutory leaving age, and to pay an indemnity if they break this agreement; they may fear the costs of uniform and general upkeep, not realizing that grants are available in case of need, and that few local authorities will exact retribution for a broken agreement, whatever the legal position may be.

Thus some children do not pass through the selection machine at all, and even if they do enter the examination and are successful, they may not take up the places awarded to them. There are undoubtedly also many failures who might have become successes under different conditions at home.

There is often a further decision to be made; what grammar school will the newly-qualified pupil attend? In an urban district there may be a choice of several, and there are often social differences in operation, for one school may be regarded as more desirable than another, either for social or for academic reasons. There may thus be a sorting out of social groups into different schools, since the heads of the more desirable ones may apply non-academic factors in their selection of pupils.

In addition, the provision of grammar-school places varies very much from one area to another, being particularly low in some rural areas. This must eventually lead to the pass list being tailored to fit the number of places available, and in consequence to widely differing standards being applied in different areas. It seems reasonable to assume that a number of children who would be perfectly capable of benefiting from a grammar-school education are being denied that opportunity. On the other hand, it must be remembered that environment factors in a rural area may be so unfavourable to a grammar-school education that, even at the age of eleven, it may be difficult to find a large proportion of children capable of undertaking the grammar-school course.

It is sometimes suggested that the intelligence of schoolchildren is falling. It must be remembered that whereas at one time only a small proportion of certain sections of the community obtained entrance to a grammar school by means of scholarships, now a much larger proportion qualify to enter these schools. In the first case an 'intellectual élite' of high I.Q. was selected, in the second, all children of over a given I.Q., which is of necessity lower than the first, are chosen. Hence it is reasonable to suppose that the average I.Q. in the grammar schools will have fallen, but it must be remembered that the number of children in these schools is much greater, and there is no sufficient reason for supposing that there are smaller numbers of children in given high I.Q. ranges. Such evidence as exists of a general fall is weak and difficult to interpret.

Children for whom a grammar-school education is not considered suitable should enter either the technical or modern schools. In practice, many will go to modern schools and from there sit a technical-school entrance examination at thirteen; in some areas it will even be necessary for them to remain in the unreorganized primary schools until the statutory leaving age of fifteen.

Many local authorities are trying out various combinations of these types of school. There are comprehensive schools for all children, with a wide range of possible subjects, and multi-lateral schools which keep separate grammar, technical and modern streams in the same school, bringing them together for certain subjects. Various bilateral combinations are being tried out: grammar-technical, grammar-modern and technical-modern.

The champions of these experiments point out that transfers from one group to another are facilitated under this system, and that children are taught to live together. The opponents express concern over the possible debasement of academic standards in the grammar-school stream in these schools.

Those in the grammar schools will follow a so-called 'academic' course culminating normally in the G.C.E. 'O' level examinations; in the technical schools it is assumed that most pupils will leave at about sixteen in order to take up apprentice-ships; and in the secondary-modern schools the majority of the pupils will leave at fifteen, although some schools do provide facilities for education beyond this point.

Leaving school

The age at which modern-school children leave influences grammar-school leaving. It is generally assumed that those who are awarded places in a grammar school will remain until they have reached a satisfactory point in the course: this is normally taken as the G.C.E. 'O' level examinations. Many children leave before they reach this point, thereby causing one of the major problems in the educational world.

There are many pressures towards early leaving. Many children become restless and tired of school once they pass the statutory leaving age, and many of them feel that there is no longer any real need for them to stay at school. If they have out-of-school friends who have already left school (perhaps because they have left a modern school at the minimum age), and who are boasting about independence and evenings no longer devoted to study, the pressures are increased. Parental influence is important here: if there is a strong assumption that the child will stay at school, then it is unlikely that he will of his own volition press to be allowed to leave and find employment; on the other hand, if the parents are indifferent or even help the child to find a job, then everything will contribute towards premature leaving.

The effects of the neighbourhood are also important; if the local customs encourage early employment and there is not a particularly strong grammar-school tradition, then children are likely to become aware of employment opportunities at an early age, and are eager to take them.

This pattern is, however, fluid, and in particular it has been suggested that the working-class attitudes which have been unhelpful to education are vanishing. In some areas, those who would normally be regarded as working class are beginning to adopt lower-middle-class behaviour patterns; they adopt the attitudes appropriate to the lower-middle-class houses in which they now choose to live. These new middle-class methods of existence may influence ideas on such subjects as the amount of education which is desirable. Certainly, better facilities for children's homework will be available in the new houses, and this simple fact may make all the difference to some children.

The chosen school is a major influence. If a high proportion of the pupils come from a working-class background, and are all exposed to the same kind of home pressures, then there will be little to prevent early leaving. If, on the other hand, the social groups are mixed, those children whose family background will favour continuing education will have some influence on the decisions made by the remainder, that is, there will be opposing pressures from the home and school environments, and often the school will win.

In a rural or a small urban district there is generally a limited choice of schools, and in many small towns there is often just one co-educational grammar school or two single-sex schools, which are attended by all the qualified pupils (and some non-qualified ones) who do not go away to a school at a distance. Thus there is, in general, a greater mixing of social classes in the country school than in the city one, and in consequence one would expect that there might be a greater tendency for children to continue education than is usual in a city. In addition, a small town will rarely offer the large number of jobs for early leavers that are offered in a city, and thus one source of temptation is largely removed.

There may be some tendency for the sons of farmers to leave school to work on the family farm, but this tendency should not be exaggerated, for if such were the intention the child might not have attended the grammar school at all. The position of the farmer's son is different from that of the city boy who has a general feeling that his chance of a 'good job' will be increased by three or four years at a grammar school.

These pressures towards early leaving will begin at fifteen and will often be accentuated over the next couple of years, as pupils leave the technical schools.

There is a certain amount of early leaving from the technical schools: this is in part due to the same pressures as those for grammar-school pupils but is also affected by the custom in some industries of recruiting apprentices at fifteen. However, most boys who take up apprenticeships have to attend their local technical colleges for some classes during the day or evening, and many of them will pursue their studies to a comparatively high level. It is to be hoped that this will be encouraged by employers.

In many continental countries apprenticeship schools are common, and in consequence young people have a better chance of continuing their general education than in this country.

In the independent schools one may expect little in the way of an early-leaving problem, as most parents will take it for granted that their sons will complete the normal school course. The parents will, in general, be responsible enough to ensure that they have sufficient money to cover the whole course, and will in many cases have taken out insurance policies to cover costs under all circumstances. (However, some parents, for social reasons, budget for a daughter to spend a limited period away at school, and are then dismayed if she wishes to stay longer and to undertake advanced work.) The children's friends at home will normally be in the same social group, and will be receiving a similar type of education, so that they should not create any early-leaving pressures.

Boarding schools as such may have a two-edged effect on the length of the school career. The distractions of normal everyday life are cut out during term, but in their place the effects of school discipline and restrictions will be felt more acutely, and the adult life glimpsed during holidays may seem exceptionally attractive. However, the other factors mentioned in the last paragraph should outweigh this.

The tragedy of this early-leaving problem lies not only in the wasted opportunities but also in the fact that many of the premature leavers will take up unsuitable careers. We have discussed in the main part of the report how it comes about that certain children are particularly in need of careers advice from school or official sources. The Youth Employment Service can do much here, although in many areas its main function lies in advising and finding suitable employment for children from the secondary modern schools, and the local officers often have to wait to be invited to local grammar schools before they can give either group or individual advice. Schoolchildren may, of course, consult the Youth Employment Officer independently, but few will recognize the need for this.

It would seem particularly desirable that grammar schools should designate one member of their staff as the careers master or mistress, and that a suitable reduction in teaching hours should be made to allow time for these extra duties. (This seems preferable to extra payment for work done outside normal hours, as it emphasizes careers advice as an integral and necessary part of the curriculum.) If it were in addition possible to set up a careers section in the school library, this would enable children to discover for themselves the requirements for various careers. The advantage of having one member of the staff as a careers specialist is that advice would be freely available at all times, and that as a result children be would helped to make wiser decisions when deciding to take up or drop subjects. Specialization is, of course, the difficulty here, but since in most schools it is customary to cut down the number of subjects studied at least one year before the pupil sits the G.C.E. 'O' level examinations, it would seem desirable to ensure that decisions are taken wisely, and that pupils, parents, and teachers, are in possession of all the facts.

A child may be influenced directly or indirectly by his parents. If they are responsible, and take an interest in the child's school career, then they will probably influence the choice of subjects, and thus of career; if, on the other hand, they are somewhat disinterested, covering up their lack of interest with 'We just want him to be happy', then the decisions made may be frivolous ones, or at least not completely thought out. It is noticeable that many parents do not even attend the careers advice interviews between their child and the local Youth Employment Officer.

After the age of sixteen most of the children receiving full-time education are in the public and grammar schools. The next step affecting the supply of scientists which we must consider comes when the decision about subjects has been made, and the pupils have taken their selected groups to G.C.E. 'O' level. At this point an even bigger decision is necessary; what next? Many will leave school at this point and either seek employment or take up some form of further training. The remainder will stay on at school, probably for the two-years' course leading to the G.C.E. 'A' level examinations, although some may remain for a shorter period until they are old enough to take up various forms of training.

The possible choices of career are now very wide. The larger engineering firms are trying to catch the scientifically trained schoolboy not only with student apprenticeships and liberal free time for attending technical college lectures and for studying, but also with the opportunity to study by means of sandwich courses and even the chance of full-time university scholarships. The biggest prizes go to those who have taken Mathematics and Science subjects at 'A' level, but there are good opportunities for those with 'O' level only.

There are in addition the traditional occupations for schoolleavers, and there is the risk that these will remain so wellknown and so popular with parents and teachers that the new opportunities available in industry will not be appreciated. Industry itself is doing much to ensure that this will not happen, by spending vast sums on advertising; schoolteachers can help by seeing that their pupils become aware of these advertisements and of what lies behind them.

Those who stay at school to take subjects at 'A' level will often decide to take their best subjects, which is a reasonable basis for selection, provided that a consistent group is chosen and that the boy or girl can see ahead to the future.

The 'A' level of the G.C.E. is commonly considered as the prelude to a university career; either an orthodox one, or a degree obtained by part-time study, sandwich courses or other means in industry. Some schools do run a general course in the Sixth Form, but usually few people take it for the full two years. Thus the choice of 'A' level subjects generally determines the choice of degree subjects.

University

This brings up the problem of university entrance. What affects a schoolboy's chance of a university career?

In most districts, university scholarships are available for most of those who obtain university entrance, although some authorities still set somewhat higher standards. However, both in these and other awards a means test is usually applied, and it is often only the lowest income groups who qualify for any aid. Those in the middle income ranges (most professional people) receive little or no benefit, and many of them simply cannot afford to cover all university expenses unaided. It must be remembered that it is in general this group who keep their children at school longest, and who provide, in proportion to their numbers, the largest group of potential university entrants. It is often children of these families who take up industrial scholarships and sandwich-course apprenticeships, but the number of these opportunities is still limited. It is to be hoped that if a means test must be applied it will in the future be applied more imaginatively.

The student who has a sufficient grounding in science may choose any one of a number of possible degree courses in the engineering and scientific fields, and may select from a wide range of subsidiary subjects, although his training will probably be less deep, thorough and varied than that of his counterpart on the Continent.

Employment of graduates

On graduation he will have little trouble in finding a suitable job; he will often have received several offers in his final year, and will have bargained for a good salary. He may, however, complain that he receives insufficient training in his new job, and that his future prospects are not as good as his initial salary led him to suppose.

Many firms now recognize that it is good policy to have some form of induction for their employees, both graduate and non-graduate. Others feel that it is desirable to let the newcomer 'find his feet' himself rather than shower him with facts which he cannot hope to assimilate immediately. There is much to be said for both points of view, and each firm must evolve the technique which suits it best. The scientifically trained person knows that he will have no difficulty in finding employment elsewhere if he feels that promotion is not coming his way quickly enough; on the other hand he should remember that he is being paid to do a job of work and not primarily to increase his own talents.

It is felt by some people that graduates in industry are not used to best advantage; that they often have to waste time on routine work, and that this represents a profligate use of our scarce resources. This problem, however, is not as clear cut as it seems. The actual technical qualifications needed for an apparently simple job may not be very high, but the job may demand a high level of intelligence in addition to some scientific training; a decision about the abandoning of one line of approach and the trial of another may involve a number of technical and other factors; unexpected difficulties which crop up may require a great deal of thought.

Industry is also criticized for using its engineers and scientists in non-technical jobs such as salesmanship, but if the product is an engineering one and the customer is an engineer, it is often necessary for the salesman to be an engineer too. However, the whole question of the 'frustration' of scientists in inappropriate work does require further research.

A further complaint is that efficient scientists and technologists are 'lost' by the laboratory and workshop through being given administrative responsibility, and that salaries and status should be so adjusted that the able man may continue to devote his full time to research without losing thereby. This again is not always desirable, for most research projects nowadays are so large that one can rarely carry them through alone; it is better to have the brilliant man at the head of the team, directing and co-ordinating the work of others even at the cost of much time spent in administration. Nor is it of necessity a loss if the scientist passes into general management; indeed such a complaint sits oddly with the complaint that there are too few technically trained people in senior management.

There will of course be occasional anomalies, and one should not penalize the genius who works alone; however, few people of this type find their way into industry, for their natural milieu is the university world.

In short, we need not (in my view) worry too much about industry's use of graduates. Most firms are cost conscious (some of them too much so) and will therefore try to utilize a scarce and somewhat expensive commodity to best advantage. However, if even one scientist is not properly used, or is frustrated, many other people may be influenced wrongly, and thus, as has been said, some research on the best use of technically trained people is desirable.

Industry itself can do much to help to satisfy its needs, and in fact is doing a great deal already. University chairs in technological subjects have been founded recently at several universities with funds raised from industry; gifts of money and equipment have also been made. Some firms encourage their staff to take part-time lecturing work in technical colleges, although many of those who would be of most use are essential to the daily running of the firm.

The shortage of science teachers is a more serious problem, and the financial aspects of the shortage seem to be the most significant. It may not be desirable to pay science teachers more than teachers of arts subjects, but there does not seem to be any alternative if we wish to maintain any reasonable standard in science teaching.

Womanpower

As we have seen, the case of women as scientists or technologists presents a number of different problems which are, in the main, connected with their function as possible wives and mothers. There is the traditional attitude that higher education for a daughter is pointless 'because she will get married and waste it'; in fact, in certain sections of the community this attitude has an adverse effect even on the upper forms of grammar schools.

More women now marry very early, and for many this must mean a very short gap between school-leaving and marriage, and very little training for a career. However, they will probably be free of child-care earlier, and many firms might find it advisable to train the more highly educated of them for routine scientific work.

It must not be forgotten that we are more ready to employ women in scientific posts than are many other countries. The one country which is very much ahead of us in this respect is Russia, but this is inevitably connected with an approach to family life which would in all probability not prove acceptable to either the men or women of this country. In consequence, while we should see that needless prejudices are removed, we must not expect miracles in this respect.

Conclusion

We have seen how many factors can determine whether or not someone becomes a scientist or technologist. Some of the barriers can be removed by simple administrative decisions; others will require a change in the climate of opinion in this country and many in consequence remain for some time. However, there are indications that the science publicity of the last decade is now paying dividends: science and engineering faculties are larger, and more children are taking science subjects at school.

We may in the next decades see a considerable adaptation of educational systems and habits to the growing needs of the country and the world for scientifically trained people.

APPENDIX 1

QUESTIONNAIRE *sent to a sample of maintained and direct grant grammar schools and independent schools in Great Britain*

1. Name of School:

   Subjects taught by Headmaster
   or Headmistress:

   Number of Pupils:

Number of Teachers	Male:	Female:
Number of Science Teachers	Male:	Female:

2. How many pupils went up to a
   University last year?

   How many pupils embarked on
   other forms of full-time
   higher education or training?

   How many pupils left last year
   (including the above)?

3. Is there a careers master
   (or mistress)?

   Is advice given to junior as
   well as to senior pupils?

4. At what age must a decision as
   to specialization be made (in
   order to select subjects for
   G.C.E., etc.)?

   What determines the choice of
   subjects for those pupils with
   no definite leanings towards
   either literary or scientific
   subjects?

   Are any difficulties
   experienced in this matter, and
   if so, of what kind are they?

   } These questions
   will no doubt
   be answered in
   the note which
   we are seeking
   from you.

APPENDIX 2

QUESTIONNAIRE *sent to a sample of County Youth Employment Officers in England and Wales*

1. Local Education Authority:

2. Number of schools whose pupils are given advice

   Secondary grammar:

   Secondary technical:

   Secondary modern:

3. Are children normally interviewed

   At their schools?

   At your office?

4. At what age are children advised about careers?

   What form does this advice take?

   lecture?

   information in personal interview?

   information given to headmaster?

   etc.

5. Are parents usually present at these lectures or interviews?

   Do you consider that parents have much influence on their children's choice of career?

6. Do you come across many cases in which pupils appear to have made the wrong choice of subject at school?

   If so, what are the most common cases?

7. Is there any other information which you think might be helpful?

BIBLIOGRAPHY

Statistical surveys

Shortages and Surpluses of Highly Qualified Scientists and Engineers in Western Europe. A Report by the Manpower Committee. The Organization for European Economic Co-operation. Paris, November 1955.

Scientific and Engineering Manpower in Great Britain: A report on the number and distribution of scientists and engineers now employed in Great Britain and a study of the likely trend in the future demand for scientific and engineering manpower. London, H.M.S.O., 1956.

Present and Future Supply and Demand for Persons with Professional Qualifications in Various Industries and Professions. London, H.M.S.O., 1949 and 1950.

Industrial employment

Report on the Recruitment of Scientists and Engineers by the Engineering Industry. Advisory Council on Scientific Policy (Committee on Scientific Manpower). H.M.S.O., 1955.

Careers in Industry. An Illustrated Review Published by *The Times.* London, 1955.

A Career for the Graduate in Industry. Federation of British Industries. London, 1954.

Report of the Conference on Industry and the Universities. Federation of British Industries. 1952.

The Graduate in Industry. Dunsheath. Hutchinson's Scientific and Technical Publications. London, 1947.

Graduate Employment: a sample survey. Political and Economic Planning. George Allen & Unwin. September 1956.

Salaries of Graduates in Industry. Planning. London, March 1957.

Graduates' Jobs. Planning. London, October 1955.

The Education and Training of Graduate Staff for Industrial Research. Federation of British Industries. 1955.

Non-Specialist Graduates in Industry. Anthea Collins. A Bow Group Pamphlet. 1955.

Directory of Opportunities for Graduates, 1957. Cornmarket Press, Ltd. London, 1957.

Universities and Industry (Productivity Report). Anglo-American Council on Productivity. November 1957.

Technological education

Technological Education in Britain. Central Office of Information Reference Pamphlets. No. 21. 1957.

The Future Development of Higher Technological Education. Report of the

National Advisory Council on Education for Industry and Commerce. London, H.M.S.O., 1950.

The Education and Training of Technologists. Federation of British Industries. London, 1949.

Criticism of Technical Education of Recently Qualified Engineers. P. Love. Institution of Mechanical Engineers. London, 1955.

Scientific Manpower. Command 6824. London, H.M.S.O., May 1946.

Memorandum on Higher Technological Education. Parliamentary and Scientific Committee. July 1954.

Technical Education. Command 9703. London, H.M.S.O., February 1956.

Universities and technology
University Development: Interim Report on the Years 1952 to 1956. University Grants Committee. London, H.M.S.O., 1957.

A Note on Technology in Universities. London, H.M.S.O., 1950.

The Availability of Places for Physics Students in Universities and Technical Colleges. The Institute of Physics. London, 1955.

The Future of the Imperial College. R. P. Linstead (Inaugural Address). London, 1955.

Proposals for the Development of the Manchester College of Science and Technology. Manchester, 1956.

Home Universities Conference, 1954. London, 1954.

From School to University. R. R. Dale, M.A., M.Ed. Routledge and Kegan Paul, Ltd. London, 1954.

Technical Education
Industry and Technical Colleges. The Federation of British Industries. September 1956.

Technical Education. P. F. R. Venables, Ph.D., B.Sc., F.R.I.C. S. Bell and Sons. London, 1955.

Technical Education for Adolescents. C. H. Dobinson, M.A. Harrap. London, 1957.

Technical Education and our Future. T. J. Drakely, D.Sc., Ph.D., F.R.I.C., F.I.R.I. North of England Educational Conference. January 1946.

Report of the Technical Colleges and Industry Conference. Federation of British Industries. London, 1954.

Technical Education in Scotland. Scottish Education Department. Edinburgh, H.M.S.O., 1953.

Schools and education
Science and Education. Professor N. F. Mott, F.R.S. Thirty-Sixth Earl Grey Memorial Lecture, 1956.

Report of the Consultative Committee on the Education of the Adolescent. London, H.M.S.O., 1927.

Liberal Education in a Technical Age. National Institute of Adult Education. Max Parrish and Co. Ltd. London, 1956.

Early Leaving. A Report of the Central Advisory Council for Education (England). Ministry of Education. London, H.M.S.O., 1954.

Secondary Education with Special Reference to Grammar Schools and Technical High Schools. London, H.M.S.O., 1939.

Parity and Prestige in English Secondary Education. Olive Banks. Routledge and Kegan Paul, Ltd. London, 1955.

Scrap the Sixth. R. C. Carrington. Article in the Journal of Education. Vol. 89. March 1957.

Industry and the Public and Grammar Schools. Federation of British Industries. 1955.

Commission on Public Schools. November 1862.

Regulations for the General Certificate of Education Examination, 1957. University of London.

Shortages of teachers

The Shortage of Science Teachers. Federation of British Industries. London, 1954.

Graduate Teachers of Mathematics and Science. A Report of the National Advisory Council on the Training and Supply of Teachers. London, H.M.S.O.

The Staffing of Grammar Schools. Egner and Young. Liverpool University Press, 1954.

The Supply and Training of Teachers for Technical Colleges. London, H.M.S.O., 1957.

Careers

Mechanical Engineering. London, H.M.S.O., 1952.

Engineering Draughtsman. London, H.M.S.O., 1954.

Scientific Womanpower

Engineering Training for Women. Verena Holmes, B.Sc. (Eng.) M.I.Mech.E. Women's Engineering Society. 1955.

Woman's Two Roles. Alva Myrdal and Viola Klein. Routledge and Kegan Paul. 1956.

Why so few women scientists and technologists? Constance E. Arregger. Article in *The New Scientist*. January 3rd, 1957.

Woman's Life and Labour. F. Zweig, Victor Gollancz. London, 1952.

Some Educational Influence on the Choice of a Scientific Career by Grammar School Girls. Nora M. Brown. British Journal of Educational Psychology, Vol. XXIII, Part III. November 1953.

Married Women in Industry. E. M. Harris. Institute of Personnel Management. London, 1954.

Married Women in the Higher Grades of the Civil Service and Government-Sponsored Research Organisations. (*Research Note*). Margot Jeffreys British Journal of Sociology. December 1952.

Employment of Married Women and Mothers of Families. International Labour Review. Vol. 63. Geneva, 1951.

Male and Female. Margaret Mead. Victor Gollancz. London, 1949.

Poverty and the Welfare State. B. Seebohm Rowntree and G. R. Lavers. Longmans. 1957.

Poverty and Progress. B. S. Rowntree. Longmans. 1941.

The War and Women's Employment. International Labour Office. Montreal, 1946.

Higher Civil Servants in Britain. R. H. Kelsall. Routledge & Kegan Paul Ltd. London, 1955.

Equal Pay. E. Marjorie Harris. Institute of Personnel Management. London, 1955.

Technological training in other countries

World Survey of Education: Handbook of Educational Organisation and statistics. United Nations Educational, Scientific and Cultural Organisation. Paris, 1955.

The Organisation of Applied Research in Europe, the United States and Canada. Volume I: *A comparative study*. Volume II: *Applied Research in Europe*. Volume III: *Applied Research in the United States and Canada*. The Organisation for European Economic Co-operation. Paris, 1954.

Trade Schools on the Continent. London, H.M.S.O., 1932.

Co-operative Education in the United States. Henry H. Armsby, Chief of Engineering Education, Division of Higher Education. U.S. Department of Health, Education and Welfare. Washington D.C., 1955.

Engineering Education in the United States. Henry H. Armsby. *Higher Education* (Semi-monthly Publication of the Federal Security Agency). Washington, D.C., 1952.

Engineering as a Career. Henry H. Armsby. *School Life*. United States Government Printing Office. Washington D.C., January 1953.

The Manpower Situation in Engineering and Science. Henry H. Armsby. Address before the Sixth Thomas Alva Edison Foundation Institute. New Jersey, 1955.

Engineering Enrollments and Degrees 1954. Circular No. 421. U.S. Department of Health, Education and Welfare. (Office of Education). United States Government Printing Office. Washington D.C., 1955.

The National Apprenticeship Program. United States Department of Labor (Bureau of Apprenticeship). Washington D.C., 1953.

The Demand and Supply of Scientific Personnel. Blank and Stigler. National Bureau of Economic Research, 1957.

Training of Operatives: Productivity Report. Anglo-American Council on Productivity. London, 1951.

The Technological Team. Henry H. Armsby. *Technical Education News*. Special Issue 1955. McGraw Hill Book Company, Inc. New York, 1955.

Report on General and Vocational Education in France. Conference on Selection and Training of Vocational Training Instructors and the Selection of Candidates for Vocational Training. Organisation for European Economic Co-operation. Paris.

Panoramic de l'Enseignement Technique. Ministère de l'Education Nationale. Paris.

Instructions Generales concernant L'Enseignement des Mathématiques. Publication du Centre National de Documentation Pedagogique. 1957.

A Brief Review of Science and Technology in Western Germany. London, H.M.S.O., 1955.

Gaining Skill. A Report of an Investigation into the Training of Industrial Apprentices in Western Germany. Birmingham Productivity Association. London, 1955.

Soviet Professional Manpower: Its Education, Training and Supply. Nicholas de Witt. Russian Research Centre, Harvard University.

Miscellaneous

Industry and Science. Manchester Joint Research Council. Manchester University Press. Manchester, 1954.

Register of Research in the Social Sciences. Cambridge University Press. August 1953, August 1954.

Report of the Third Conference of Industrial Research. Directors and Managers. Federation of British Industries. London, 1953.

Notes on Grants Awarded by the Department of Scientific and Industria Research to Research Workers and Students. London, H.M.S.O., 1952.

The Royal Society of Arts, 1754–1954. Hudson, Derek and Luckhurst. Kenneth William. London, 1954.

Prediction of Vocational Success. Thorndike, E. L. and others. New York. 1934.

New Developments in Industrial Leadership. Sir Walter Pucky and Sir Geoffrey Vickers. Polytechnic Management Association. London, 1955.

Education for Management: Productivity Report. Anglo-American Council on Productivity. London, 1951.

Recent Copies of '*The New Scientist*'.

Recent copies of '*Technology*' (published by *The Times*).

INDEX